SEE THE FIRST STEPS: FOOTBALL ANALYTICS

Using Microsoft Excel to

Visualize 2019 NFL Football Data

DR. RODNEY J. PAUL

SEE SPORTS, LLC

TABLE OF CONTENTS

PRE-GAME

How to Use this Book:

Welcome to *See the First Steps: Football Analytics* from SEE Sports, LLC. As it relates to anyone interested in the first steps to approaching football analytics, this book only assumes a basic knowledge of the sport of football including the general rules, positions on the field, scoring system, etc. For anyone who would like to introduce themselves, their child or family member, friend, or otherwise to the sport of football and would like an overview of the basic structure of the game, please see our friends at www.rookieroad.com/football/ for a detailed introduction to the sport in general.

For junior high school and high school students using this book, a variety of terms which are important for the SAT, ACT, and AP Statistics are noted in this book and are identified through underline. These include terms and concepts that are commonly covered on these exams and in the course.

For computer data analysis and the visualization of football analytics, this book uses Microsoft Excel. Excel is available for free to all students, through their school email address. You can find a link to obtain the software here: https://www.microsoft.com/en-us/education/products/office. When using Excel, the book uses color-coding, in addition to pictures, to help to guide where the various functions, buttons, and drop-down menus are located in the software. As described in detail in Chapter 3, items on the Ribbon Tabs are shown in blue, items on a ribbon are shown in green, and steps requiring some action (such as highlighting) are shown in italics. Once you get started, these are likely to become second nature, but we hope the pictures and color-coding will ease your first steps into this new world.

For adults, we hope you will enjoy this book as much as any student and would encourage you to share with your children, grandchildren, nieces and nephews, friends, etc. We believe doing visualizations of various football analytics together would be a fun way to increase interest and skill-level in math and statistics. If you are new to Excel, the charts shown are not only useful for football, but could enhance reports, research, and presentations you may have for work as they add to general skills and are certain to liven up any written document.

The data we use in this book is available for free from www.pro-football-reference.com. It is a tremendous resource with constantly updated and archived football statistics which we highly recommend and use ourselves. Since they do update their website, check the column headers over time to be sure they have not added new variables, and if they do, some of the column labels (A, B, …) may have changed. If this happens, follow the header names to create the charts shown in this book as it relates to column labels.

A key point for anyone dealing with Excel for the first time is that if a function, drop-down menu, or button does not appear on the screen, first try clicking on the chart (or different points on the chart) and see how the options available to you change. Anything that is not in the instructions given in this book (directing you to specific ribbon tabs, ribbons, etc.) is likely accessed by clicking somewhere on the chart to give you the options seen in our instructions.

It is our sincere hope that you enjoy this book and through its use will gain deeper insights into math, statistics, football analytics, and the game of football itself. We hope it is not only fun to look at for last season's stats, but that you can use the methods and techniques shown to enjoy the season as it progresses and each season moving forward. Thank you.

CHAPTER 1

FOOTBALL ANALYTICS

A key word in both business and in sports in recent years has been analytics. Although it has been around for a long time, the word entered the public sphere in sports after Michael Lewis's excellent book *MoneyBall*. The coverage of the use of analytics by the baseball's small-market Oakland A's in both the book and the movie brought about a consciousness to a topic that many had likely used before by various names, but now fit into a specific category.

What is meant by analytics? In many ways, it's difficult to pin down a precise definition that would please everyone. Dictionary.com gives three definitions for analytics. They are as follows:

1) The science of logical analysis

2) the analysis of data, typically large sets of business data, by the use of mathematics, statistics, and computer software

3) the patterns and other meaningful information gathered from the analysis of data.

As beginners starting our journey into the world of football analytics, what do these definitions mean? It is far easier to begin with the last two definitions, rather than the first. In definition (2) we see that analytics starts with data. Various pieces of statistical information, sometimes numbering in the millions or more, are analyzed in analytics. How is the data analyzed? First, theory is grounded in mathematics and statistics. Properties of variables in the data set are calculated and this begins our information process. Relationships between various pieces of data are explored, as noted in definition (3) above, and specific patterns are noted and scientifically tested. This means it generally follows the scientific method, where a specific hypothesis is noted, compared to an alternative hypothesis, and tested using statistical analysis. This is where definition (1) now comes into play as the whole process is supposed to occur in a logical framework resulting in output or outcomes toward some actionable item or items. In other words, analytics uses data to test theories that result in actionable items for a person or group. This could be a business, a government, an individual, or a football team.

When asked to develop the Sport Analytics major for Syracuse University, I needed to figure out the key puzzle pieces to put into place to prepare students for jobs working for sports teams and organizations. To do this, I focused on a curriculum including lots of math, computer programming skills, modeling of relationships between data, business theory, and communication of findings. Each of these are important. Mathematics gives the underlying theory behind the generation and relationships between the numbers investigated. Computer language programming is needed to gather, clean, present, and sort the wide range of data needed to do analysis and modeling of important relationships. Visualization of results through charts and graphs allows for the presentation of sometimes complex ideas in a straightforward fashion. Various business theory courses provide a foundation for understanding and interpreting company and consumer behavior. Communication skills allows a person to provide insights to different interested parties in a manner that will be most effective for them. Combining all of these factors together leads to what analytics is to me, a practical way to use data to guide decision-making. At the end of the day, we are not doing the math for math's sake, we are looking to provide helpful information.

Although all of the above-mentioned skills are important to analytics, we need to find a logical place of entry for people to start to use analytics for football or for anything else. You do not need lots of high-tech skills to get started in football analytics. You simply need a desire to study the game of football, the statistics surrounding it, free data available online, and basic spreadsheet software to perform analysis and visualize data in the form of charts and graphs. To do this, we'll use Microsoft's Excel program, which is part of their Office suite program, and is available free of charge to students through the Office 365 Education program. It can be accessed online directly through: https://www.microsoft.com/en-us/education/products/office by providing your school email address. If you are not attending school, hopefully you have this available to you through work or other means, if not, there are other low-cost options in obtaining the software listed through the website link above.

So, with Excel and some data that we will download from the excellent football website www.pro-football-reference.com, we can take our first steps into the analysis of data through analytics! Why use football? Did you ask why use football? It's only the most popular sport in the US, with tons of fans nationwide and around the world. Statistics are plentiful, they are used during broadcasts, shown on websites (and even old school in newspapers and magazines), and fans love to participate in fantasy football, where they draft players for teams of their own and earn points based upon statistical performances each week of the NFL season to try to outcome their opponents. Beyond that, it's fun.

Math takes such a bad rap for students across the country. In many ways, this is profoundly sad. Students at a young age are told that math is difficult and that it's just something "you need to do". These statements and attitudes push people away from math and math-related disciplines. Students do not see the general usefulness of math-related disciplines in society. However, when we watch football, we immediately see the usefulness. We know that it takes 10 yards to earn a first down. Yards per rush or reception are important terms discussed by people across the country every fall. 300-yard passing days are considered special as are 100-yard games rushing or receiving. The list goes on-and-on; football is a mathematical game.

Why and how do teams use football analytics? Analytics are used in the sport of football as it relates to in-game action. The decision to run or pass the ball on offense can be guided by analytics. Playing coverage or blitzing on defense is an analytical decision. Going for it on fourth down rather than punting or kicking a field goal is predicated by an understanding of the underlying probabilities of success of each of these events. In short, every decision on the field can be guided by analytics. As technology has improved, more data has become available for coaches and players to use. Gaining an edge through analytics can be the difference between winning and losing, making the playoffs or not, and earning a championship for a team.

Beyond the on-field action, analytics are used in personnel decisions. Determining which players to draft, what free agents to keep or allow to leave, and what trades to make (or not make) are guided by analytics. Insights gained from available statistics and their analysis help scouts, front office personnel, and the general manager make decisions on their roster.

Analytics are also important to the business-side of the football relationship. What price to charge for tickets, which game to broadcast on Sunday Night Football, what player might make a good sponsor for a product, etc. are all ways analytics can be incorporated into decision making. In short, you would be hard-pressed to find any area of the sport where using data analytics would not be helpful.

Therefore, we start our journey with the first steps. Although the overall field of analytics may be vast and somewhat intimidating, my goal is to provide you with ways to study football on your own, provide your own analysis and predictions, and be able to communicate these findings with your friends, family, and others. Data analytics can be fun. So, let's get the crowd into a frenzy, have the referee blow the whistle, and kick off our adventure into football analytics.

CHAPTER 2

PRE-GAME — BACKGROUND STATISTICS INFORMATION

The proper use of terminology is often essential to being recognized as trained in a discipline. Virtually every industry has its own language that, to outsiders, often does not make sense. In statistics, the same phenomenon happens. Whether we are talking about standardized tests, courses, or actual professions, the use of the proper words in the proper places carries considerable weight.

Population vs. Sample — Parameter vs. Statistic

The first distinction made in statistics is the difference between a <u>population</u> and a <u>sample</u>. A <u>population refers to all observations that can be made</u>. It is the entire pool of people or things with a common feature. Anyone that fits the category cannot be excluded from a population by definition. A <u>sample</u>, on the other hand, is a <u>subset of a population</u>. A sample includes a number of observations from a population that are collected by a defined procedure. Samples are drawn to make inferences and test hypotheses.

This distinction leads to the key difference in terminology between a <u>parameter</u> and a <u>statistic</u>. A <u>parameter is a measure that describes a population</u>. A <u>statistic is a measure that describes a sample</u>. A measure, in these examples, would include things we will discuss such as means and standard deviations. In this book and in the practice of football analytics in general, we will be using statistics taken from samples of NFL players.

Quantitative vs. Categorical Data

When we think of football statistics, we typically envision <u>data measured on a numerical scale</u>. This type of data is called <u>quantitative data</u>. An alternative form of data, which can be equally if not more important, is called <u>qualitative</u> or <u>categorical</u> data. <u>Qualitative data breaks the sample into groups</u>. Simple forms of qualitative data may take the form of a binary variable, where there are two possibilities.

<u>Categorical data expands this possibility into multiple categories where the data could fall</u>. The distinction here is that each observation is placed within a group and is distinguished by that grouping. For instance, the outcome of a football game is different between college football and the NFL. In college football, given their overtime system, all games end with a winner or a loser. Therefore, each game will have a binary outcome and the categorial data for game outcome is labeled as either a win or a loss. In the NFL, however, games can and do end in ties during the regular season. Hence, there are three categories that an NFL game outcome can fall into, a win, a loss, or a tie.

One key piece of categorical data we will observe for our NFL player data is position. Each player is given a particular position on the field. When we are studying receiving, various types of position players catch passes on offense. These include wide receiver, tight end, and running back. In some cases, offensive linemen are placed in an eligible position on the field and may catch passes (even for touchdowns!) at different times throughout the season. These categories help to distinguish various items we wish to describe and put them in proper context. For instance, what is the average number of receiving yards per reception for a running back compared to a wide receiver? Given the way the positions on the field are structured, we expect running backs would be more likely to catch shorter passes, on the average, than wide receivers. Therefore, when we distinguish by category, we can better make comparisons between similar types of players.

Descriptive vs. Inferential Statistics

When looking at NFL or any other statistical data, the statistics we generate or are provided to us serve two purposes. <u>One key function of statistics is to describe data</u>. The process of describing data can sometimes be referred to as exploratory data analysis (EDA). This is often, if not always, the first step in the data-driven decision-making process. Describing data can be both analytical and graphical in nature. We can describe the sample of data we have through observing the measures of center like a mean or median. We can observe measures of spread through variance and standard deviation. In addition, we can graph or plot the data to examine its shape and spacing. When comparing two statistics to each other, we can describe the data by looking at correlations or by graphing scatterplots.

<u>Inferential statistics</u>, on the other hand, <u>uses data drawn from samples to make inferences about the population from which it was drawn</u>. We use a sample of data to make some statement or test a theory about characteristics of a population. For instance, consider the notion of some quarterbacks being "too short" to successfully play in the NFL. We can use data from a sample of NFL quarterbacks to attempt to illustrate this point. However, the sample is not the population, so even if shorter quarterbacks were less successful than taller quarterbacks in a certain sample, it does not mean that it will always be the case for every possible quarterback who could play in the NFL.

CHAPTER 3

PRE-GAME – INTRODUCTION TO EXCEL

Throughout this book, we are going to use Excel to house our data, make some simple calculations from the data, and visualize/plot a variety of charts using football statistics from *Pro Football Reference*. Before being able to start on the fun stuff, it's incredibly useful to do some pre-game analysis and get our "playbook" in order. When teams get new coaches, either at the head coaching level or in terms of the coordinator (offensive and defensive) positions, there is typically a learning curve as it relates to the terminology. Everyone on the team needs to be "on the same page" meaning that they know what each other is talking about.

This is the same for us as we take our first step to do football analytics on our own. Excel is a spreadsheet where we are going to store data and be able to use it to provide valuable information. Since we use Excel exclusively in this book, we will break down the blank worksheet you see on your screen when you open the program. When you open Excel for the first time, this is the interface you will see:

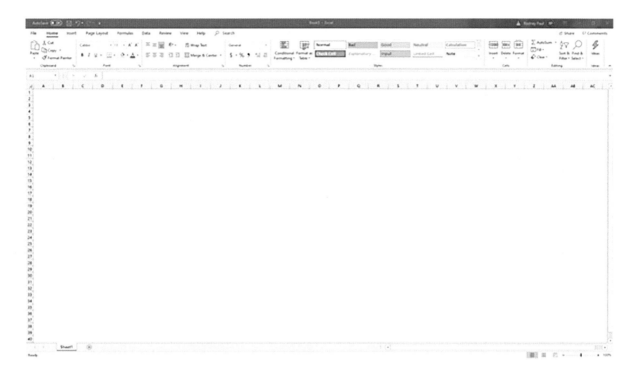

We will focus only on the parts of the program we will use in the book. There are a ton of other features and once you begin to see what you can do with the program you will likely want to explore more on your own. For our purposes, let's start with the top and work our way down. The top of the program is in green and gives the name of the notebook, the user name (if logged in) and the ability to put autosave on/off, save your work the icon to the right of the autosave toggle button, which is a picture of an old disk, a back arrow, etc.

Immediately below this green row, we see a set of words arranged horizontally across the page starting from the far left. These are *Ribbon Tabs*. For each ribbon tab listed, there will be multiple options available for you to use when you click on the name.

File	Home	Insert	Page Layout	Formulas	Data	Review	View	Help	🔎 Search

In this book, we will mainly use 5 elements from the ribbon tabs, **File, Home, Insert, Data, and View**. The **File** tab is where you can save your work or load previous work back into Excel. It is also a place where you could print your charts if you would like to. When you click on File, you will see the following:

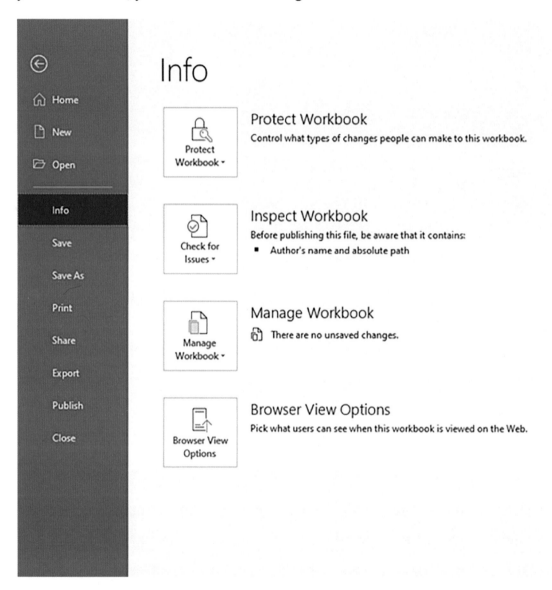

New will create a new worksheet for you. You can have multiple worksheets open at the same time. **Open** will allow you to open a saved Excel file (spreadsheet) you previously worked on. **Save** will allow you to save your work. You can use **Save As** to save an updated file of the same spreadsheet with a different name. I personally recommend saving your work often, typically with new file names. When you make changes to a spreadsheet, you may not ultimately like what you did. You could have eliminated data you really wanted or removed a chart you wanted to use. If you saved a previous version, you could open that version at any time to use the information or start a new path from that incarnation. I like to use the name that is representative of the data we are working on (i.e. "NFL_Passing_Data_2019" coupled with a date "NFL_Passing_Data_2019_6_29_20"). If I save the files multiple times in one day, I will also add time to the title "NFL_Passing_Data_2019_6_29_20_930AM"). You could also be descriptive in the title in terms of what you generated. For example, if you made a scatterplot chart, you could put scatterplot in the title. **Print** will allow you to print your file.

Home returns you to this introductory screen. **Insert** we will use specifically for our charts. When you click on Insert you see the following in the **Ribbon** below the **Ribbon Tabs**:

We will use the **Charts** section of this Ribbon, which is in the middle of the page:

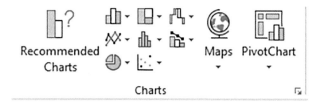

The 8 boxes above the Charts title will be our access points to create the variety of charts and graphs we will construct throughout the book.

We also will use the **Data** Ribbon Tab. When you click on **Data** you see the following Ribbon:

Primarily, we will use the **Sort and Filter** section to arrange the data in specific ways to help us create charts. **Sort** is on the left, which gives various options including the quick alphabetical sorts to the left of the larger button, **Filter** will create ways for use to sort data directly on the spreadsheet itself, without having to click back on the Ribbon.

At times we will also use the View section. This section will mainly be used for the **Freeze Panes** option, which will allow us to view the headers as we scroll down the screen.

Immediately above the spreadsheet area, there is a blank white box. This is the *Formula Bar* and we will use this to enter names (for titles of charts and other things on the visualizations we create).

The *Worksheet* itself is below the formula bar. The columns are labeled by letter, starting with A. They are seen across the top row (in gray – not numbered) of this part of the screen. The rows are labeled by number, starting with 1. They are seen down the first column (in gray – no corresponding letter).

The rectangular boxes that populate the screen above are called **Cells**. **Cells** will contain labels, data, and formulas. The active cell, the one you are working on, will be seen with a green outline (the rectangle will have green borders). Each cell will hold one piece of information (a data point or a label). Individual cells are identified by their Column/Row combination, such as A1 or C12.

Below the worksheet, ***Sheet Tabs*** are shown. You can open multiple worksheets in a single Excel file. When you start, you will only see **Sheet1** (Worksheet 1). When you click on the + in a circle to the right of **Sheet1**, it will open a new sheet for you.

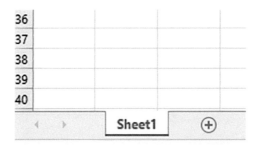

Although this is only a small fraction of what Excel can do, it should suffice for what we want to be able to accomplish in our first steps in football analytics.

CHAPTER 4

MEASURES OF CENTER/LOCATION
— PASSING STATISTICS 2019

Any type of data set you work with will typically be summarized for a variety of purposes. People like quick summaries of data as they provide information and feedback in small doses. While summaries could either be "spot on" as a Patrick Mahomes pass or "way off" as a Nathan Peterman attempt that invariably seemed to end up in an opposing defender's hands, the tendency to produce data summaries is constantly anticipated and provided.

The first summary point typically presented is the <u>mean</u> or average of a variable. A variable is any statistic that we are observing and typically will be represented by a column in our spreadsheet. The <u>mean is the sum of all the values divided by the number of observations</u>. The number of observations is referred to as *n*. Lower case *n* refers to a sample from a population, while capital N refers to the entire population. The mean of a sample is referred to as "x-bar" or $\bar{x}$. If a backup quarterback had 4 completions on the season resulting in gains of 5, 7, 13, and 21 yards, he would have averaged 11.5 yards-per-reception – simply add the 4 values and divide by *n*=4. The equation for calculating the mean of a sample is:

$$\bar{x} = \frac{\sum_i^n x_i}{n}$$

The mean is very useful for giving the central location of a distribution. It does not provide any information of how spread out the distribution is or if the mean ever actually appeared in the sample.

A variation of the mean which is sometimes useful is what is referred to as a trimmed mean. In a trimmed mean, you drop a fixed number of observations from each end of the distribution (i.e. highest and lowest values) and calculate the mean of the remaining observations. In our example above, if we drop the backup QB's highest (21) and lowest (5) completions, we are left with 2 completions for 20 yards or a trimmed mean of 10. In this case, the trimmed mean is less than the overall mean due to the dropping of a rather long reception (in this data set) of 21 yards. Trimmed means can be useful when trying to minimize or eliminate the influence of extreme values or what we call outliers. An outlier is a data point that is very different from the rest of the data in the sample. When an NFL team goes on a trip to London, England to play a regular season game or a college football team travels to Hawaii (for that wonderful 11:59 PM ET kick-off), the travel distance for that game is typically an outlier compared to other games they play in a season.

Another useful variation on the mean is a weighted mean. A weighted mean is calculated by multiplying each observation (x) by a weight (w) and dividing their sum by the sum of the weights. A weighted mean may be used when some observations are more valuable than others. Suppose we are considering yards gained per play when a football team is in a close game as opposed to when they have a substantial lead (a blowout). In the blowout scenario, the team is likely looking to use the clock to run out the time remaining and not give the opponent an opportunity to make a comeback. In this situation, the offensive yards-per-play will typically be lower, but is not necessarily a good representation of how effective an offense is in an NFL game. Therefore, one may want to weight those plays differently compared to when the team is in a close game. A problem with weighted means is the choice of actual weights to use, which is both tricky and difficult, but if everyone knows and realizes the weights chosen, the weighted mean could provide more value than the actual mean.

Another measure of center that can be useful as a summary of data is the <u>mode</u>. The <u>mode is the most common value in a distribution. It is the observation that occurs most frequently</u>. In a distribution of Wide Receiver receptions, it would be the most common number of receptions for receivers in the data set. For coaching experience, it would be the most common tenure length among all coaches. In some data sets, values seldom, if ever, repeat themselves, therefore the mode would not be useful in describing that distribution. Otherwise, it can be useful to know what value is most common, as it is the one that typically would be the most likely to happen again.

Measures of Center/Location Using Quarterbacks in Excel

Let's start our investigation into measures of center/location and football by delving into statistics on quarterbacks from last season (2019).   Our data for this section comes from the plethora of statistics available on *Pro Football Reference* (<u>www.pro-football-reference.com</u>). When you access their homepage, you will see a screen that looks something like below:

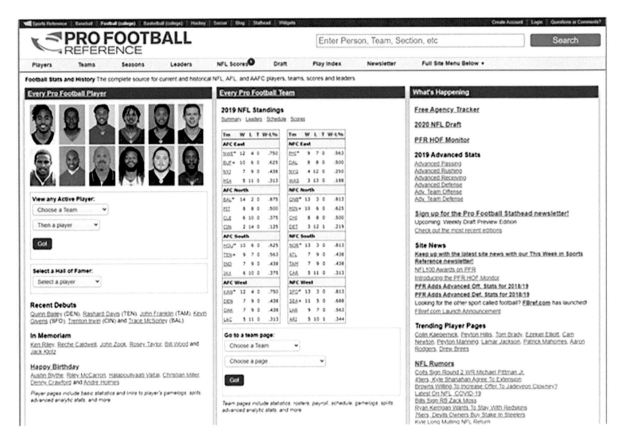

Once there, hover your mouse over Seasons (middle-to-top left of the page – below the "ce" in REFERENCE in website title) and select 2019 NFL – Player Stats- Passing. It will bring you to the following page (https://www.pro-football-reference.com/years/2019/passing.htm

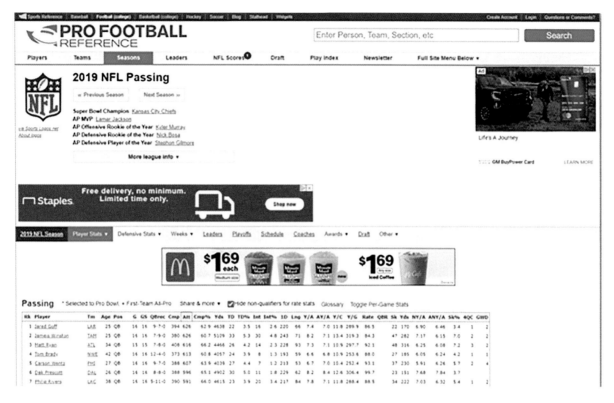

Under Share & more (using the down arrow) (above Att (in yellow) and Cmp%), use the drop-down menu to choose "Get as Excel Workbook". This will download a file on your computer. (You may receive a warning, but you can allow the file to open in Excel). Open the file and Excel will open with the output from the file. Once you open the file, you will see the following:

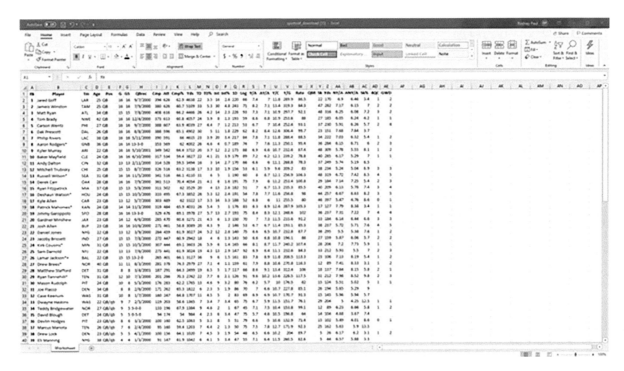

Before working with the data, you may need to "Enable Editing" which would be across the top of your screen in Excel.

The data is sorted by Att (Attempts). You can sort by any other column by choosing Data and then Sort to choose which variable to sort by and in which direction (we'll do some sorting of data in later chapters). Let's use the data as is and investigate a few variables that you likely already know in terms of center/location.

First, to keep the headers on the variable names visible, you need to freeze that row. Go to View (top middle in grey below the green row at top), when you click on View a new set of options will appear that will look like this:

Rk	Player	Tm	Age	Pos	G	GS	QBrec	Cmp	Att	Cmp%	Yds	TD	TD%	Int	Int%	1D	Lng	Y/A	AY/A	Y/C	Y/G	Rate	QBR	Sk	Yds	NY/A	ANY/A	Sk%	4QC	GWD
1	Jared Goff	LAR	25	QB	16	16	9/7/2000	394	626	62.9	4638	22	3.5	16	2.6	220	66	7.4	7	11.8	289.9	86.5		22	170	6.9	6.46	3.4	1	2
2	Jameis Winston	TAM	25	QB	16	16	7/9/2000	380	626	60.7	5109	33	5.3	30	4.8	243	71	8.2	7.1	13.4	319.3	84.3		47	282	7.17	6.15	7	2	2
3	Matt Ryan	ATL	34	QB	15	15	7/8/2000	408	616	66.2	4466	26	4.2	14	2.3	228	93	7.3	7.1	10.9	297.7	92.1		48	316	6.25	6.08	7.2	3	2
4	Tom Brady	NWE	42	QB	16	16	12/4/2000	373	613	60.8	4057	24	3.9	8	1.3	193	59	6.6	6.8	10.9	253.6	88		27	185	6.05	6.24	4.2	1	1
5	Carson Wentz	PHI	27	QB	16	16	9/7/2000	388	607	63.9	4039	27	4.4	7	1.2	213	53	6.7	7	10.4	252.4	93.1		37	230	5.91	6.26	5.7	2	4
6	Dak Prescott	DAL	26	QB	16	16	8/8/2000	388	596	65.1	4902	30	5	11	1.8	229	62	8.2	8.4	12.6	306.4	99.7		23	151	7.68	7.84	3.7		
7	Philip Rivers	LAC	38	QB	16	16	5/11/2000	390	591	66	4615	23	3.9	20	3.4	217	84	7.8	7.1	11.8	288.4	88.5		34	222	7.03	6.32	5.4	1	2
8	Aaron Rodgers*	GNB	36	QB	16	13-3-0		353	569	62	4002	26	4.6	4	0.7	189	74	7	7.6	11.3	250.1	95.4		36	284	6.15	6.71	6	2	3

Choose Freeze Panes, using the drop-down arrow, and select "Freeze Top Row" (middle option). This keeps your headers "frozen" when you scroll down the screen. Now scroll down to the last row of information and we will make some calculations at the end of the data. In row 105 (leaving a blank row in 104), let's calculate the mean for completions (Cmp), attempts (Att) and yards (Yds). Completions are the number of successful passes the quarterback threw on the season, attempts are the number of passes thrown, and yards is the number of yards gained on the completions. We'll start with completions in column I. In I105, type

=average(I2:I103)

In the above expression = tells Excel you are using a formula, the formula is average (to take a mean) and the terms in parentheses give you the range of data for Excel to compute the mean (you can also highlight these cells by clicking on i2 and then scrolling down to the end of the data at i103). When you type this in the cell, you will get 111. Since the column is narrow, Excel naturally rounds to the three digits to the left of the decimal. If you expand the length of column I (by clicking on the barrier between I and J (above the header row) and dragging it to the right), you will see more digits displayed. To get the average for attempts (Att) and completions (Cmp), you could retype the formula (changing the column), but an easier way is to copy-and-paste. Left-click on cell i105 for it to be highlighted in a green outline. Now right-click on the cell and take the option of "Copy" (another alternative is to hit CTRL-C). Paste (by using Paste – under Home on the top left of the screen or by right-clicking on the cell and choosing "Paste" or by using CTRL-V) into J105 and then L105. This will give you the mean value for each of these variables. When completed, you will see the following:

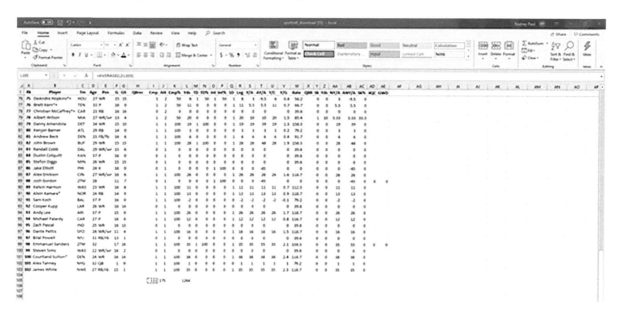

We see the average number of completions for all players who threw at least one pass in 2019 was 111, the average number of attempts was 175, and the average yardage the QB threw for was 1,264. What do these numbers tell us? Something, but not necessarily anything overly useful. Why? First the data set contains every player who threw a pass. This includes running backs and wide receivers on trick plays, punters and kickers on fakes, etc. These are likely not very good representations of quarterback play and may not be helpful. Perhaps we can gain more insights if we restrict the data in some way. Since the data is already sorted by Attempts (Att), let's restrict the sample to QBs who threw 400+ passes on the season. This would include down to row 27 (26th ranked in terms of attempts as the first row is the header row) and our sample would include Lamar Jackson.

To work with this subset, first open a new tab at the bottom of the screen by clicking on the + to the right of the Worksheet tab (bottom left). This will open a new blank spreadsheet tab. Go back to the original Worksheet tab (click on it), then highlight rows 1-27 (left-click on the 1 in dark grey to the left of column A (next to header Rk). Copy (CTRL-C) this data, go to the new worksheet tab, and paste (CTRL-V) in cell A1.

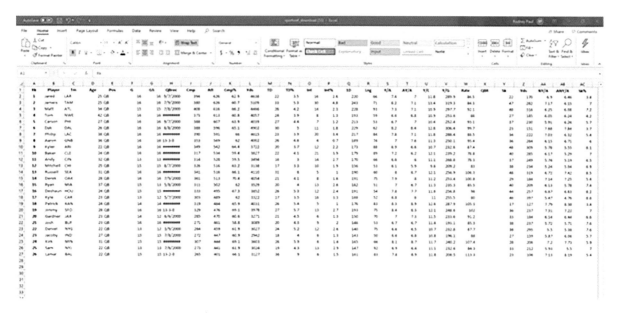

Now, let's repeat the exercise of computing the mean by using =average for the three columns of interest (I, J, L) for rows 2-27. Example:

=average(I2:I27) in I29 (similar for J and L)

In our subset, we now see that the means of each of the variables have grown considerably as we have omitted anyone that did not throw 400 or more passes in 2019. The mean of completions (Cmp) is 332.0769, the mean of attempts (Att) is 521.6154 and the mean of yards (Yds) is 3,806.462. These are likely to be more useful figures in analyzing quarterbacks, but remember that we left out plenty of other QBs who played part of the season due to injury or other factors such as Drew Brees and Teddy Bridgewater (who split time in New Orleans due to the injury to Brees). When reporting any summary statistics, including measures of center/location, be sure to note the sample. Is it the full sample? Is it restricted? In what way? This helps others be able to interpret and use the statistics you calculate.

How close is the mean of this subset of QB data to the trimmed mean? Remember, the trimmed mean eliminates values at each end of the distribution of data – so in this case it would eliminate the highest and lowest values for each variable. The general structure of the command (formula) to calculate the trimmed mean is (do not type into Excel):

=trimmean(array, percent)

The "array" is our column of data (i.e. I2:i27) and the percent is what you choose to trim from the sample. 0.1 would trim 10% (5% from top and 5% from bottom), while 0.2 would trim 20% (10% from top and 10% from bottom). We can use both options to calculate the trimmed mean by typing the following in cells I30 and I31:

=trimmean(I2:I27,0.1)

=trimmean(I2:I27,0.2)

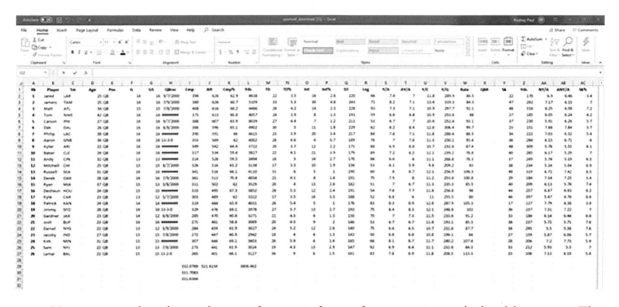

You can see the trimmed mean does not change by a great margin in either case. The bigger the outliers and the smaller the sample size, however, the more a trimmed mean will differ from the sample mean. Copy and paste cells I30 and I31 to J30 and J31 and L30 and L31 to see the trimmed means for attempts (Att) and Yds (Yards).

With the computation of means and trimmed means in our back pocket, let's turn our attention to another measure of location, the <u>median</u>. The <u>median is the middle number on a sorted list of data</u>. In odd-numbered samples, the median is simply the observation in the direct middle (equal number of observations on either side). For even-numbered samples, the median is the average of the middle two observations. It may seem to be inferior to the mean at first, as the mean uses all the data points, while the median only uses the middle data point (or average of the middle two), but the median has its advantages. The median helps with outliers on either end of the distribution. An outlier will impact the mean, especially in small samples, but the median is not affected as it will always take the middle value (it is only affected in the sense that the outlier is included in the sample and counts as an observation).

In the presence of outliers (extreme values in the sample), the median is likely a better estimate of the center than the mean. The median is often described as a robust or resistant estimate of location. Robust or resistant means the value taken by the statistic is not dramatically influenced by outliers. While the median is robust (resistant), the mean is not. A trimmed mean can be thought of as a compromise between the use of the mean and the median for location. The trimmed mean aims to eliminate the influence of outliers, just like the median, but it uses more data for its computation.

To compute the median of the variables of interest in our data set is straightforward. Let's leave a row between the previous computations and the median, so we'll start in cell I33. In I33 type =median(I2:I27). The median will now appear in cell I33. Copy that cell and paste into J33 and L33 to get the median of attempts and passing yards as well. To help distinguish what we did, I'll label each computation in column H next to the computed figures. The median is less than the mean for completions (Cmp) and Attempts (Att), but is greater than the mean for Yards (Yds). We can see the even number of observations at play here as the median of completion is 327.5, as that is not an observation in our data, nor is it possible (you cannot half-complete a pass).

With these figures calculated, we now return to the data itself to describe some of the less familiar quarterback data provided. The statistics in the table are described below:

- Name – Quarterback Name

- Team – Team played for in 2019

- Age – Age on game day

- QBrec – record in terms of win/loss on the season

- Cmp – Pass Completions

- Att – Pass Attempts

- Cmp% - Pass Completion Percentage

- Yds – Yards Passing

- TD – Touchdown passes

- TD/Att – Touchdowns per Attempt

- Int – Interceptions

- Int/Att – Interceptions per Attempt

- 1D – 1st Downs Passing

- Lng – Long pass on the season

- Y/A – Yards per Attempt

- AY/A – Adjusted Yards per Attempt

- Y/C – Yards per Completion

- Y/G – Yards per Game

- Rate – Quarterback Rating

- QBR – ESPN Quarterback Rating (not available for 2019 season)

- Sk – Sacks

- Yds – Sack Yardage

- NY/A – Net Yards per Attempt

- ANY/A – Adjusted Net Yards per Attempt

- Sk% - Sack Percentage

- 4QC – 4th Quarter Comebacks

- GWD – Game Winning Drives

After providing the name of the quarterback, the team he played on in that season, his age (at that time), position, games (G), games started (GS), his record (QBrec), we get to the start of our examined columns with completions (Cmp) and attempts (Att). His completion percentage (Cmp%) is presented next, followed by Yards (Yds). I expect you are familiar with Touchdowns (TD – throw for a score) and Interceptions (Int – pass was picked off by the opposing team) and they are presented next, along with their percentages in terms of attempts (i.e. TD/Att). 1D is first downs made by the quarterback, his long pass on the season is presented in the column named Lng.

The next few columns contain useful ratios in terms of yardage. Y/A is yards per attempt, Y/C is yards per completion, and Y/G is yards per game. These are helpful figures as they put yards passing in context. Some teams throw the ball very often, either by design or due to them often trailing in games. Typically and naturally, quarterbacks playing in these situations will accumulate more yardage than other quarterbacks, but it does not necessarily mean they are better at their position. Yards per attempt adjusts yardage for how many times the quarterback threw the ball, while Yards per completion adjusts for how many completed passes the quarterback made. In each case, we gain further insight into the QBs play; with attempts we see how often he threw the ball (with yards adjusted), while with completions we obtain insight into how yardage was impacted by the number of completions. Highly accurate QBs who play in pass-heavy offenses will not see as wide of a gap between Y/A and Y/C as inaccurate passers in run-first systems. Also, many highly accurate quarterbacks may play in a short-passing game offense (such as the West Coast Offense), where short passes often substitute for runs and yards per attempt and yards per completion will often be less than quarterbacks who do not play in these types of systems.

AY/A, adjusted yards per attempt, is a bit more complicated in terms of football analytics, but is a useful figure provided by *Pro Football Reference*. This figure takes passing yards and adds 20 multiplied by touchdowns (20*TD), then subtracts 45 multiplied by interceptions (45*Int). This figure rewards quarterbacks for touchdowns (which, in some cases, could have gone for more yardage but was limited in yards by the receiver crossing the goal line) and punishes quarterbacks for interceptions.

Quarterback Rating (Rate) is a convoluted and complicated calculation which differs between the NFL and college football. For the NFL, the rating consists of four individual parts, typically labeled a-d. Part a takes completions divided by attempts and subtracts 0.3 from that ratio. It then multiplies that figure by 5. In part b, it computes yards passing divided by attempts and subtracts 3 from that ratio. That figure is then multiplied by 0.25. Part c divides touchdowns by attempts and multiplies that ratio by 20. Part d is computed by dividing interceptions by attempts and multiplying that ratio by 25. After that, you subtract that figure from 2.375. Finally, all four parts (a-d) are added together, divided by 6, and then multiplied by 100. The rating scale goes from 0 to 158.3 (perfect rating). To achieve a perfect rating, a quarterback needs at least a 77.5% completion percentage, 12.5 average yards per attempt, 11.875% touchdown-to-interception ratio, and no interceptions. Although much maligned, at least this statistic is consistently calculated and has been recognized by the NFL since 1973. QBR is quarterback rating as computed by ESPN, however there are no observations for this for the 2019 season in *Pro Football Reference*, so we will not discuss how it is computed here.

The last few columns presented for quarterbacks in *Pro Football Reference* begins with Sacks (Sk). A sack occurs when a defensive player tackles a quarterback behind the line of scrimmage, denying the passer an opportunity for an attempt and possible completion. Sacks could be due to poor blocking by the offensive line, tight ends, and running backs or could be due to the quarterback himself. Quarterbacks who are slow in their drop backs and release, hold on to the ball too long, and/or are not mobile tend to be sacked more often. Additionally, teams that throw the ball more often (either by design or due to trailing in a game) will often accumulate more sacks on the quarterback as well.

Notice in our 2019 data set that Matt Ryan (ATL), Kyler Murray (ARI) and Russell Wilson (SEA) were each sacked 48 times. This likely occurred due to different reasons. Some has to do with the offensive line and blocking, other may have to do with a relative lack of mobility (Ryan), inexperience (Murray), or perhaps holding on to the ball and taking the sack as opposed to throwing into coverage to risk an interception (Wilson – notice his interceptions (5) and interception rate (1) based on his 516 attempts). Sack Yards (Yds – notice it has the same header as passing yards – so when working with this data would suggest relabeling as Syds for sack yards) and Sack Percentage (Sk%) are also shown to put sacks into better context.

Two more complicated statistics are also shown that use sacks, NY/A and ANY/A. NY/A is net yards per pass attempt and ANY/A is adjusted net yards per pass attempt. Net yards per pass attempt (NY/A) is calculated by subtracting sack yards from passing yards to form the numerator and then dividing by the sum of pass attempts and sacks. Adjusted net yards per pass attempt (ANY/A) incorporates rewarding touchdowns (TD) and punishing interceptions (Int) for quarterback play in addition to incorporating the sack data. The numerator for ANY/A is (Passing Yards – Sack Yardage + (20*TD) – (45*Int)) and the denominator is (Attempts + Sacks). Notice Patrick Mahomes had the highest NY/A and ANY/A of our subset of QBs with 7.79 and 8.38, respectively. This came about through his high yards per attempt (Y/A), great TD to Int ratio (26-to-5) and low sack rate (only sacked 17 times on season (3.4%)). While his truly spectacular season might not immediately be obvious with passing yards and touchdowns, which are count statistics, as he was limited due to games lost due to injury, these ratios provide a glimpse of his dominance on the football field in 2019.

The last two columns provide some information about clutch performances by quarterbacks and will provide us with an opportunity to explore the mode. 4QC is 4th quarter comebacks and GWD is game winning drives. These statistics are count variables that account for performances at or near the end of games. 4QC is defined as a quarterback-led scoring drive in the 4th quarter when the team trailed by one score. This includes drives that did not take the lead, but to qualify the team must have tied or won the game. GWD is when the quarterback leads an offensive scoring drive in the 4th quarter or overtime that leads to a win. In our top subset of quarterbacks, you can see that Russell Wilson (SEA), Deshaun Watson (HOU), and Josh Allen (BUF) each had 5 game winning drives in 2019. Wilson (SEA), Allen (BUF), and Jimmy Garoppolo (SF) all had 4 fourth quarter comebacks.

For both of these variables, what is the mode and how does it compare to the mean? Let's compute for 4QC by typing in AD29

=mode(ad2:ad27)

And then copying and pasting that to AE29 (to compute mode for GWD). In cells AD30 and AE30 compute the mean. This is shown below, with the QB name and team (by using View – Freeze Panes – first option – with cell AD2 highlighted) for 4QC and GWD:

The mode for 4QC is 1, while the mode for GWD is 2 in this sample of QB data. These are the most frequently observed values for the 26 quarterbacks chosen. In both cases, the mode is smaller than the average value seen in the sample (shown below the mode).

Rk	Player	Tm	4QC	GWD
1	Jared Goff	LAR	1	2
2	Jameis Winston	TAM	2	2
3	Matt Ryan	ATL	3	2
4	Tom Brady	NWE	1	1
5	Carson Wentz	PHI	2	4
6	Dak Prescott	DAL		
7	Philip Rivers	LAC	1	2
8	Aaron Rodgers*	GNB	2	3
9	Kyler Murray	ARI	1	2
10	Baker Mayfield	CLE	1	1
11	Andy Dalton	CIN		
12	Mitchell Trubisky	CHI	3	3
13	Russell Wilson*	SEA	4	5
14	Derek Carr	OAK	2	3
15	Ryan Fitzpatrick	MIA	3	4
16	Deshaun Watson*	HOU	3	5
17	Kyle Allen	CAR	0	1
18	Patrick Mahomes*	KAN	1	1
19	Jimmy Garoppolo	SFO	4	4
20	Gardner Minshew	JAX	3	3
21	Josh Allen	BUF	4	5
22	Daniel Jones	NYG	1	2
23	Jacoby Brissett	IND	2	2
24	Kirk Cousins*	MIN	1	1
25	Sam Darnold	NYJ	2	3
26	Lamar Jackson*•	BAL	1	2
		Mode	1	2
		Mean	2	2.625

Bar Graphs of Center/Location

It is much easier to show people statistics in graphical form than in tabular (table) form. Charts and graphs can bring data to life and they do not need to be overly complicated to be effective. In fact, it is most often the case that a simple chart or graph can be much more interesting and effective than one which is super-detailed and complicated. With this in mind, let's start by investigating the use of bar graphs with our QB data. Let's start with passing yards (Yds) in column L. Follow the steps below:

1) *Highlight L1 to L27* (click and drag down with the mouse to highlight the cells in this column, then release)

2) Move the mouse to Insert (to the right of Home – near upper left-hand corner), click on Insert (new options in a ribbon will appear)

3) Go to the Charts section of this ribbon (middle of screen).

Charts

4) Click on the first button to the right of "Recommended Charts" on the top left. It will create a bar chart for you. When clicking on the down arrow in the box, it gives various options including 2-D and 3-D column charts and bar charts. Let's use the first option, 2-D column charts.

After clicking on that option, a new window appears that will look like this:

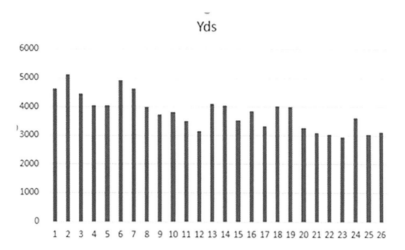

We now have our first chart. Let's improve its details by adding the Quarterback names to the horizontal axis.

5) Click on **Chart Tools** (top in the green) and click on Design. (You may already be there – if option is not available – click on the chart first and it gives new screen options – you have different screen options if on the spreadsheet or on the chart).

6) Go to Select Data in the Data section of **Chart Tools**-Design. A new window appears after you click.

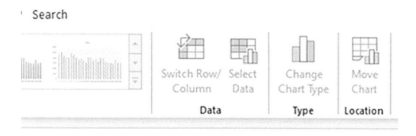

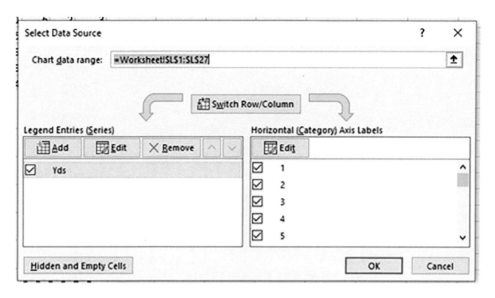

7) Go to Edit under the Horizontal (Category) Axis Labels – when new window appears, highlight B2:B27 – the QB name will now appear under the (column) bar chart (do not highlight B1 as that is the header, we just want the QB names). Click OK.

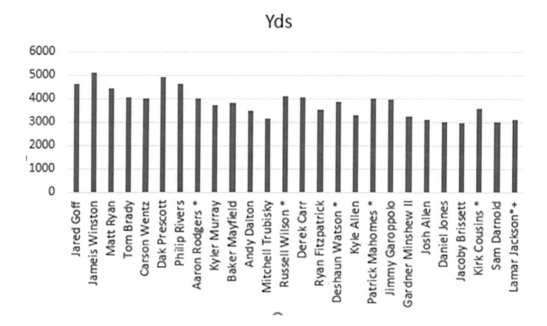

8) Add a title to the vertical axis by going to Add Chart Element (far left on the ribbon), click the down arrow, and click Axis Titles – Primary Vertical.

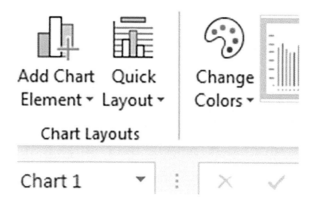

9) Click on the box that says, "Axis Title" on vertical axis and type "Passing Yards" and click Enter

10) Click on chart title (currently says "Yds") and type "Passing Yards – 2019 NFL Season" to give the chart a title.

11) Let's make the chart a full screen by moving it – go to Location (ribbon – last thing on right) – new window appears – click New Sheet – click OK – now appears as own sheet in Excel

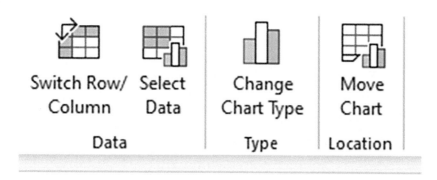

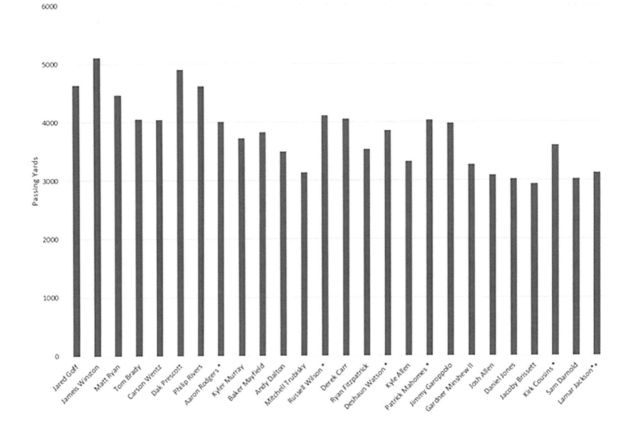

From the chart, you can see quarterbacks in our sample with the highest passing yardage on the season (Winston, Prescott) and those with the lowest (Brissett, Darnold, Jones).

Let's do the same chart, but alter it slightly by making a chart of touchdown passes (TD) of the top 20 quarterbacks and putting them in descending order. First, go back to the worksheet by clicking on the worksheet tab at the bottom left of the Excel screen – this will bring you back to your data. Follow the steps below:

1) Click on Data in Ribbon Tab

2) In the middle of the Ribbon, you will see the Sort & Filter section – click on Filter

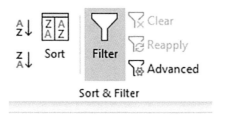

3) Now the first row will appear with down arrow options

4) Click on the down arrow in column M – TD (if want to make column larger, click on the line to the right of the M in gray and drag it to the right – so the column will be larger)

5) New window appears – click on Sort Largest to Smallest

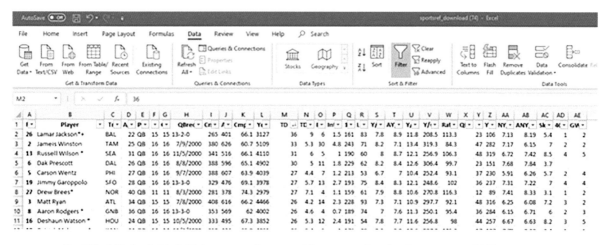

6) Highlight M1:M21 to get the top 20 quarterbacks in terms of TD Passes

7) Click Insert (Ribbon Tab) – Charts – 2D Column

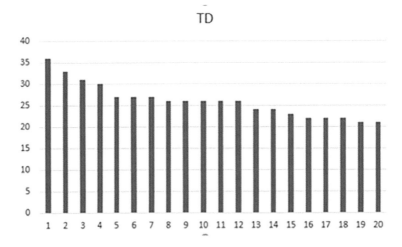

8) Add Vertical Axis Title by: Add Chart Element (Ribbon) – Axis Titles – Primary Vertical – click on where it says, "Axis Title" and type "TD Passes"

9) Add names to horizontal axis by Data (Ribbon) – Select Data – new window appears – Horizontal (Category) Axis Labels – Edit – highlight B2:B21 – click OK

10) Add title – click on current title "TD" and type to change to "TD Passing Leaders – 2019 NFL Season"

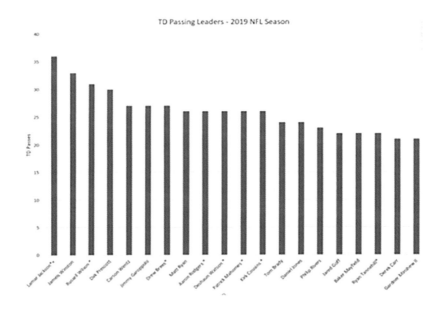

We can see that Lamar Jackson led the way, followed by Winston, Wilson, and Prescott. The data is now arranged from highest to lowest, which many people prefer when reading a column bar chart. You can always get data in order from highest to lowest or lowest to highest by using the filter in Excel and sorting. When you read, you are reading left to right, it typically makes sense to have the highest values on the left-hand side of the chart and then taper off as you move right across the screen/page.

With our first steps, we see that we can use column charts to highlight league leaders in passing categories. We saw the yardage leaders and the touchdown leaders and how the ordering differs. Although he was at the bottom of our subset in terms of yards passing, Lamar Jackson was the clear leader in terms of touchdowns. We will return to his MVP 2019 season in a later chapter to further investigate his great performance.

From the passing leader chart, we see an interesting conclusion. The quarterback with the greatest number of passing yards in 2019, Jameis Winston, was not commonly suggested as the best quarterback in the NFL. Passing yardage, by itself, may not be a great indicator of success because teams that play from behind will have quarterbacks that often accumulate high yardage totals as they need to throw the ball more often. In Winston's case, other factors (such as interceptions) played a key role as to why his performance was not lauded in Tampa Bay in 2019 and was not kept as the team's quarterback moving forward in 2020. Often, more statistics are needed to paint a clearer picture of success or failure, not just one factor that might be associated with performance.

Moving Forward: Suggested Story Telling with Data to Pursue:

1) Use a column chart to compare Jameis Winston's interceptions to other QBs.

2) Chart the leaders in Yards per Attempt and Yards per Completion. Which figure do you think is better in analyzing quarterback performance?

3) Which QBs were sacked most often in 2019? Did these QBs also throw a high number of interceptions?

CHAPTER 5

ADVANCED PASSING STATISTICS

In this chapter we will explore the advanced passing statistics available on *Pro Football Reference*. This data expands what we can study for quarterbacks and focuses mainly on the breakdown of passes between the yardage in air versus the yardage gained after the catch. An overview of advanced passing stats is shown below, followed by a discussion on how to put the statistics in context.

Advanced Passing Stats — *Pro Football Reference*

Advanced Passing: Air Yards

Advanced Passing Share & more ▾ ☑Hide non-qualifiers for rate stats Glossary

| Air Yards | Accuracy | Pressure | Play Type |

					Games							Passing						
Rk	Player	Tm	Age	Pos	G	GS	Cmp	Att	Yds	IAY	IAY/PA	CAY	CAY/Cmp	CAY/PA	YAC	YAC/Cmp
1	Jared Goff	LAR	25	QB	16	16	394	626	4638	4825	7.7	2388	6.1	3.8	2250	5.7
2	Jameis Winston	TAM	25	QB	16	16	380	626	5109	6486	10.4	3249	8.6	5.2	1860	4.9
3	Matt Ryan	ATL	34	QB	15	15	408	616	4466	5009	8.1	2816	6.9	4.6	1650	4.0
4	Tom Brady	NWE	42	QB	16	16	373	613	4057	4638	7.6	2233	6.0	3.6	1824	4.9
5	Carson Wentz	PHI	27	QB	16	16	388	607	4039	4878	8.0	2235	5.8	3.7	1804	4.6
6	Dak Prescott	DAL	26	QB	16	16	388	596	4902	5539	9.3	2984	7.7	5.0	1918	4.9
7	Philip Rivers	LAC	38	QB	16	16	390	591	4615	5025	8.5	2430	6.2	4.1	2185	5.6
8	Aaron Rodgers*	GNB	36	QB	16	16	353	569	4002	5005	8.8	1993	5.6	3.5	2009	5.7
9	Kyler Murray	ARI	22	QB	16	16	349	542	3722	3987	7.4	1870	5.4	3.5	1852	5.3
10	Baker Mayfield	CLE	24	QB	16	16	317	534	3827	4516	8.5	2007	6.3	3.8	1820	5.7
11	Andy Dalton	CIN	32	QB	13	13	314	528	3494	3991	7.6	1843	5.9	3.5	1651	5.3
12	Mitchell Trubisky	CHI	25	QB	15	15	326	516	3138	4108	8.0	1729	5.3	3.4	1409	4.3
13	Russell Wilson*	SEA	31	QB	16	16	341	516	4110	4836	9.4	2402	7.0	4.7	1708	5.0
14	Derek Carr	OAK	28	QB	16	16	361	513	4054	3364	6.6	1932	5.4	3.8	2122	5.9
15	Ryan Fitzpatrick	MIA	37	QB	15	13	311	502	3529	4467	8.9	2264	7.3	4.5	1265	4.1
16	Deshaun Watson*	HOU	24	QB	15	15	333	495	3852	4396	8.9	2166	6.5	4.4	1686	5.1
17	Kyle Allen	CAR	23	QB	13	12	303	489	3322	3965	8.1	1649	5.4	3.4	1673	5.5
18	Patrick Mahomes*	KAN	24	QB	14	14	319	484	4031	4273	8.8	2076	6.5	4.3	1955	6.1
19	Jimmy Garoppolo	SFO	28	QB	16	16	329	476	3978	3106	6.5	1819	5.5	3.8	2159	6.6

Many of the key stats are repeated from the basic passing statistics. Name, team, age, position, games, games started, completions, attempts, and yards passing are again included in this data set. The newly added statistics attempt to break down quarterback play into how far they typically throw the ball, how far the ball travels on completions, and the yardage gained after the catch. Let's look at each individually:

- IAY – Intended Air Yards – air yards on all pass attempts, whether completed or not

- IAY/PA – Intended Air Yards divided by pass attempts

- CAY – Completed Air Yards – total yards completed passes traveled in the air beyond the line of scrimmage

- CAY/PA – Completed Air Yards divided by pass attempts

- YAC – Yards after catch on passing plays

- YAC/Cmp – Yards after catch divided by completions

Context:

Intended Air Yards (IAY) and its average per attempt (IAY/PA) illustrate how far the quarterback throws the ball downfield. Some statistics, such as completion percentage, are helped by consistently "checking down" on throws to RBs coming out of the backfield or short pass options. Completion percentage is also helped by a short-passing game strategy by the offensive coordinator/coaches. IAY helps to create a distinction when observing passing statistics by seeing how far the QB typically throws the ball in the air, reported as an average. Completed Air Yards (CAY) takes the same concept but applies it only to completed passes. This statistic, and its average per attempt, indicates how far down the field the quarterback throws the ball when the pass is caught by a receiver. We would expect longer pass attempts are generally more difficult to complete than shorter pass attempts. A ratio of IAY to CAY can be useful in determining if the QB is successful downfield in his passes. Yards After Catch (YAC) and its average per completion is also useful in seeing the additional yardage gained by a receiver after a pass is completed.

In the case of all three statistics, the quarterback is not the only party involved in success or failure. To be able to throw the ball downfield, a quarterback needs protection. Therefore, the offensive line (and any other blockers on the play) needs to be successful to give the QB the time and opportunity to succeed downfield. A mobile quarterback who can throw on the run may be able to overcome poor protection, but it is difficult to succeed downfield without successful pass blocking. In addition, the receivers will play a big role. A pass may be incomplete due to an errant throw, good defense, or poor receiving skills. Some QB statistics will apparently reflect poor performance, when in reality, it could have been due to drops on the part of receivers or receivers not being able to create space between themselves and defensive backs. YAC might appear to be the realm of receivers, rather than quarterbacks, but quarterbacks who are able to successfully lead receivers, hit them in stride, and are able to throw passes that reach the receiver when they outrun their defenders will also be partially responsible for this statistic. Of course, coaching and the appropriate game plan will also play a big role in these statistics as well.

Advanced Passing: Accuracy

Advanced Passing   Share & more ▾   ☑Hide non-qualifiers for rate stats   Glossary

Air Yards | **Accuracy** | Pressure | Play Type

					Games					Passing								
Rk	Player	Tm	Age	Pos	G	GS	Cmp	Att	Yds	Bats	ThAwy	Spikes	Drops	Drop%	BadTh	Bad%	OnTgt	OnTgt%
1	Jared Goff	LAR	25	QB	16	16	394	626	4638	17	15	1	27	4.4%	123	20.2%	437	71.6%
2	Jameis Winston	TAM	25	QB	16	16	380	626	5109	11	22	2	23	3.8%	124	20.6%	421	69.9%
3	Matt Ryan	ATL	34	QB	15	15	408	616	4466	19	27	1	17	2.9%	86	14.6%	443	75.3%
4	Tom Brady	NWE	42	QB	16	16	373	613	4057	6	40	0	34	5.9%	118	20.6%	419	73.1%
5	Carson Wentz	PHI	27	QB	16	16	388	607	4039	16	10	1	28	4.7%	106	17.8%	431	72.3%
6	Dak Prescott	DAL	26	QB	16	16	388	596	4902	9	14	1	36	6.2%	86	14.8%	451	77.6%
7	Philip Rivers	LAC	38	QB	16	16	390	591	4615	13	16	3	25	4.4%	88	15.4%	439	76.7%
8	Aaron Rodgers*	GNB	36	QB	16	16	353	569	4002	3	31	1	24	4.5%	114	21.2%	401	74.7%
9	Kyler Murray	ARI	22	QB	16	16	349	542	3722	18	24	4	17	3.3%	92	17.9%	378	73.5%
10	Baker Mayfield	CLE	24	QB	16	16	317	534	3827	20	19	2	30	5.8%	93	18.1%	362	70.6%
11	Andy Dalton	CIN	32	QB	13	13	314	528	3494	14	17	7	27	5.4%	92	18.3%	362	71.8%
12	Mitchell Trubisky	CHI	25	QB	15	15	326	516	3138	8	7	3	28	5.5%	93	18.4%	377	74.5%
13	Russell Wilson*	SEA	31	QB	16	16	341	516	4110	9	20	3	17	3.4%	91	18.5%	376	76.3%
14	Derek Carr	OAK	28	QB	16	16	361	513	4054	9	28	2	25	5.2%	53	11.0%	399	82.6%
15	Ryan Fitzpatrick	MIA	37	QB	15	13	311	502	3529	15	7	3	28	5.7%	87	17.7%	358	72.8%
16	Deshaun Watson*	HOU	24	QB	15	15	333	495	3852	6	15	2	21	4.4%	80	16.7%	367	76.8%
17	Kyle Allen	CAR	23	QB	13	12	303	489	3322	14	25	1	28	6.0%	77	16.6%	353	76.2%
18	Patrick Mahomes*	KAN	24	QB	14	14	319	484	4031	6	19	0	25	5.4%	85	18.3%	359	77.2%
19	Jimmy Garoppolo	SFO	28	QB	16	16	329	476	3978	6	7	2	28	6.0%	64	13.7%	377	80.7%

The second tab on *Pro Football Reference* under Advanced Passing presents measures of accuracy of quarterbacks. Building off of the previous section, these statistics help to determine why a pass may have been incomplete and attempts to separate some of the blame of incompletions between the quarterback and his receivers. The key new stats introduced here are:

- Bats – Number of passes batted down by a defender at or behind the line of scrimmage

- ThAwy – Number of passes that were determined to be thrown away

- Spikes – Number of passes that were spiked to stop the clock

- Drops – Number of passes dropped by receivers

- Drop% - Percentage of pass attempts dropped, excluding throwaways and spikes

- BadTh – Number of throws determined to be poor throws

- Bad% - Percentage of pass attempts that were bad throws, excluding throwaways and spikes

- OnTgt – Number of throws determined to be on target

- OnTgt% - Percentage of pass attempts that were on target to a receiver, excluding throwaways and spikes

Context:

The first four stats listed above help to quantify passes which were ultimately incomplete. Bats occur at or behind the line of scrimmage. Bats are partially determined by protection (offensive line and others) and by the quality of the pass rush (defense) but are also likely to be a function of height of a quarterback and his release point. The reason scouts and team management are often afraid of short quarterbacks is not only their possible inability to see passing lanes, but also the higher likelihood of having a pass knocked down at the line. This may not show up as much in an NFL study, as shorter quarterbacks who do not have the ability to avoid bats are likely not in the league for long (something we call survivor bias – we only observe those that make it in the league, the others no longer play).

Throwaways result in incompletions, but they typically will not result in a possibility of an interception. So, whereas throwaways would seem to immediately be a negative statistic, it could represent intelligence and maturity in a quarterback. Why would a quarterback throw a ball away? It could be to avoid a sack, or it could be that the intended target and other options were covered and forcing the play in that situation would not be worth the risk. Throwing the ball away to avoid a sack could be a function of protection, as a leaky offensive line may lead to many sacks and throwaways, or it could be due to quarterbacks not wanting to be hit or giving up on a play too soon. Coaches and scouts need to distinguish between these factors to effectively evaluate talent. Mobility of a quarterback will also play a key role here as movement when the pocket breaks down creates opportunities to complete passes which could be thrown away by immobile quarterbacks.

Spiking the ball to stop the clock before halftime or the end of a game is counted as an incomplete pass attempt. Therefore, removing spikes from pass attempts is a good idea as this "pass" never had a chance to be complete in design or execution. Drops are incompletions that get assigned to a receiver. When a receiver (which could be a wide receiver, running back, tight end, or other eligible player) drops a ball that could have been caught, incorporating this statistic serves to lessen the blame on the quarterback for the throw. Although it's unrealistic to think every catchable ball will be caught, keeping track of drops allows for a comparison to receivers on other teams to potentially help project a quarterback onto a different roster (or help to project when free agent receivers are brought into a team's offense).

Bad throws (BadTh) and on target throws (OnTgt) use subjective decisions from statisticians to further assign praise or blame to quarterback play. Bad throws are passes that the receiver would not be able to catch, while on target is where the receiver would be expected to catch the pass. As before, the quarterback himself may not fully be responsible for this as pass protection and route running by receivers is important, but a quarterback who consistently racks up bad throws is likely to struggle to keep an NFL job. On the other hand, quarterbacks who are on target, but may suffer from drops, are likely to be given a chance by a team with a better receiving lineup or the team itself may choose to draft or bring in better receivers to help the quarterback and team succeed.

Drops, bad throws, and on target passes are also shown as percentage of attempts, which helps to put these numbers on a comparable scale for quarterbacks who throw more/less often than their peers. Spikes and throwaways are not included in attempts for these percentages, which further adds to their validity. Having accuracy stats helps teams to better evaluate quarterbacks and helps in game planning (and conversely in planning defensive strategies against quarterbacks).

Advanced Passing: Pressure

The third tab on Advanced Passing is pressure. Beyond the stats available on the other tabs, this tab includes sacks and other disruptions to quarterback performance. The key new stats in this section are:

- Sacks – defense tackles a quarterback for a loss of yardage

- PktTime – Pocket time – average time between the snap and (a) throwing the ball or (b) the pocket collapses

- Bltz – times quarterback was blitzed by opposing defense

- Hrry – times quarterback was hurried by opposing defense

- Hits – number of hits a quarterback took on the season

- Scrm – scrambles – number of rushes on plays designed as passes

- Yds/Scr – Yards per scramble average

Context:

Quarterbacks take sacks for a variety of reasons. One reason is poor protection which leaves little time to make a throw. Another reason is that a quarterback holds the ball too long. This could occur due to not seeing open receivers or deciding not to throw the ball due to good defensive coverage. Blitzes can lead to sacks and other forms of pressure. A blitz is when the defense rushes players other than defensive linemen (linebackers and/or defensive backs). A quarterback may face more blitzes based upon the schedule they play (there is an unbalanced schedule in the NFL, so a team may face teams who blitz more than average or less than average) or based upon their abilities. Quarterbacks who are not as mobile or are slow in their drop back into the pocket, in addition to quarterbacks who tend to hold on to the ball for longer periods of time, will often be blitzed more than others.

Hits is a variable that tabulates how many times the quarterback gets hit. This does not only include sacks, but also counts when taking a hit as or after the ball is released. Hits can be as physically diminishing to a quarterback as a sack. Pocket time (PktTime) measures how long the quarterback has the ball from the snap to when they throw the ball or until the pocket (area they drop back into after the snap of the ball) collapses (via a sack or a scramble out of the pocket). Like sacks, pocket time is a function of protection by the offensive line and other players and the quarterback's own physical abilities and tendencies. The number of times a quarterback escapes the pocket to run is noted as a scramble. Some quarterbacks scramble often, while others tend to do this infrequently. Yards per scramble notes the success (or failure) in yards rushing when the quarterback escapes the pocket. Scrambling by quarterbacks, particularly to earn first downs with their legs, is a positive attribute that contributes to team success.

Advanced Passing – Play Type

The last tab on the advanced passing statistics page on *Pro Football Reference* includes information about the run/pass option (RPO) and play action.

- RPO statistics are broken down into the number of these plays the quarterback ran (Plays), the total yards gained on these plays, whether it be run or pass (Yds), the number of pass attempts in the RPO setting (PassAtt), Passing Yards when the quarterback passed out of the RPO (PassYds), and Rush Yards out of the RPO (RushYds)

- For Play action – the number of pass attempts out of play action (PassAtt) and passing yards gained from these attempts (PassYds) are shown

Note: When working with this data, you will likely want to change the headers, so you do not repeat the same variable names in different settings (i.e. overall yards passing vs RPO yards passing). This is true in other areas of *Pro Football Reference* as well and is a good thing to keep in mind before you start doing calculations or making charts from the data.

Context:

A run/pass option is designed to give the quarterback the option to hand the ball off to a running back, keep the ball and run himself, or throw a pass after choosing not to hand off/run the ball. While the option is seen in college and high school football, it has been less prevalent in the pros. In recent years, however, offensive coordinators have used quarterbacks in an RPO setting as it allows for another layer of deception and can be difficult for the defense to defend (especially if the quarterback is dangerous as a runner).

Play action is when a quarterback fakes a handoff to the running back and then attempts to throw a pass. Here, again, deception is the key as play action can "freeze" linebackers and/or safeties, leading to a greater opportunity for a receiver to become open.

QB-Advanced – <u>Bar Charts</u>

Now that we have a grasp on the types of data available on advanced passing statistics, let's use some of them to explore bar charts. Bar charts are a simple way to convey information. Bar charts are different from the column charts of last chapter as they are horizontal in nature. Greater values are represented by a longer line stretching left to right on a bar chart. To begin with bar charts, follow the instructions below:

2-D Bar Chart

1) Download data from https://www.pro-football-reference.com/years/2019/passing_advanced.htm

2) *Highlight data from IAY/PA* (**L2:L104**)

3) **Insert** – Charts – 2D Bar

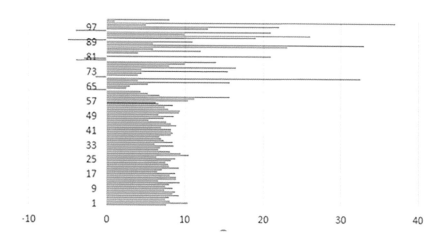

4) **Chart Tools** – Design – Select Data – **Horizontal (Category) Axis Labels – edit** – *highlight Player column (do not include header)* (**B3:B104**)

Select
Data

IAY/PA

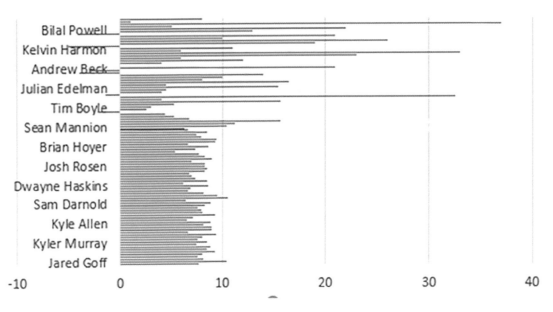

5) 5) *Filter by clicking on chart* – **then filter button icon – uncheck Select All** in categories– then **check 1st 20 players (check each box)** [there are other options to Filter – as we will see in later chapters]

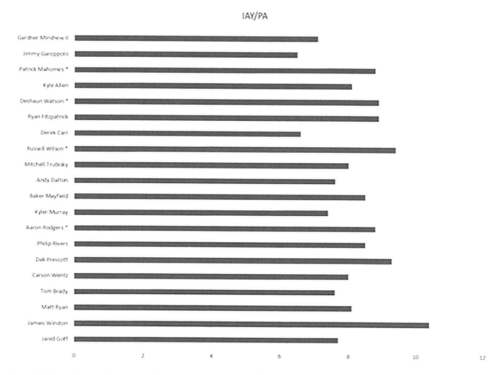

6) Add a Descriptive Title – double-click on IAY/PA (the current chart header) and write out title

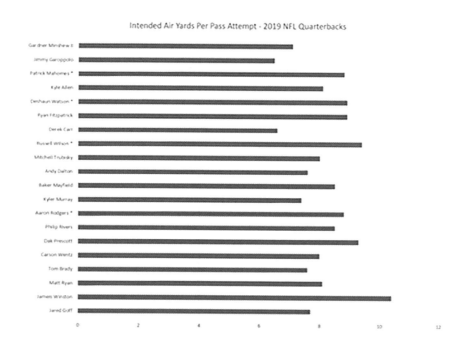

7) For this one – let's add Data Labels – Chart Tools – Add Chart Element – Data
Labels – Outside End

Add Chart
Element ▾

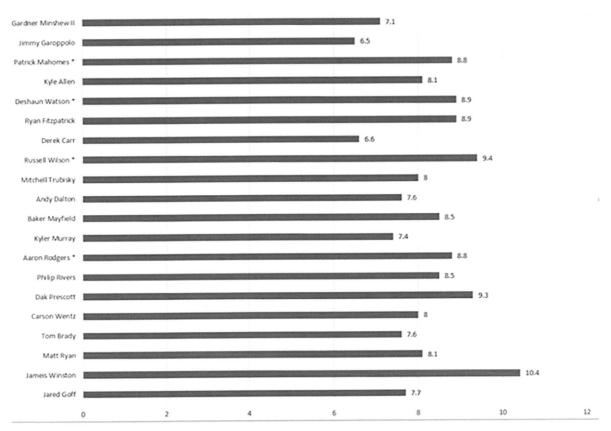

Intended Air Yards Per Pass Attempt - 2019 NFL Quarterbacks

Gardner Minshew II	7.1
Jimmy Garoppolo	6.5
Patrick Mahomes *	8.8
Kyle Allen	8.1
Deshaun Watson *	8.9
Ryan Fitzpatrick	8.9
Derek Carr	6.6
Russell Wilson *	9.4
Mitchell Trubisky	8
Andy Dalton	7.6
Baker Mayfield	8.5
Kyler Murray	7.4
Aaron Rodgers *	8.8
Philip Rivers	8.5
Dak Prescott	9.3
Carson Wentz	8
Tom Brady	7.6
Matt Ryan	8.1
Jameis Winston	10.4
Jared Goff	7.7

8) Let's highlight the highest and lowest of this subset – *double-click on series for
Jameis Winston – change color to Red – double-click on series for Jimmy
Garoppolo – change color to Green* (in these cases only the one bar should be
identified (squares on each corner) – otherwise all bars will change color)

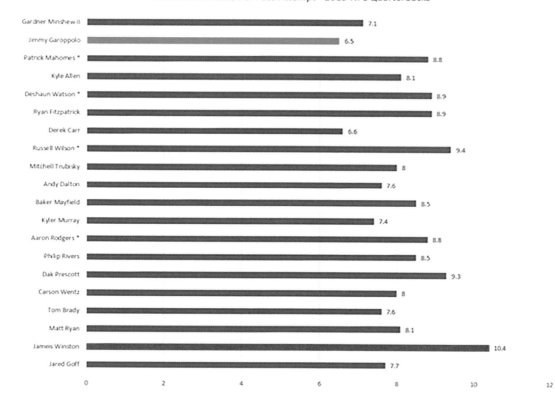

Intended Air Yards Per Pass Attempt - 2019 NFL Quarterbacks

Gardner Minshew II	7.1
Jimmy Garoppolo	6.5
Patrick Mahomes *	8.8
Kyle Allen	8.1
Deshaun Watson *	8.9
Ryan Fitzpatrick	8.9
Derek Carr	6.6
Russell Wilson *	9.4
Mitchell Trubisky	8
Andy Dalton	7.6
Baker Mayfield	8.5
Kyler Murray	7.4
Aaron Rodgers *	8.8
Philip Rivers	8.5
Dak Prescott	9.3
Carson Wentz	8
Tom Brady	7.6
Matt Ryan	8.1
Jameis Winston	10.4
Jared Goff	7.7

Context:

This chart shows the average Intended Air Yards per Pass Attempt (IAY/PA) for the top 20 Quarterbacks in the NFL in terms of pass attempts in 2019. Jameis Winston had the highest average at 10.4 and Jimmy Garoppolo had the lowest at 6.5 (among this sample). Winston tended to throw the ball further downfield than any of the other quarterbacks. Quarterbacks who threw for similar average Intended Air Yards per Pass Attempt were Russell Wilson and Dak Prescott. Each averaged over 9 intended air yards per pass attempt. An interesting question to pursue is how did these quarterbacks fare in yardage? In touchdowns? In interceptions? Garoppolo averaged fewer than 7 intended air yards per attempt, as did Derek Carr. How do their other stats compare to Winston, Wilson, and Prescott? You will find that when you pursue some data inquiry, you are likely to discover more questions. As you continue to explore and expand, you will start to find some interesting relationships that could provide valuable insights.

QB Advanced – 2-D Stacked Bar Chart – CAY and YAC per completion

1) Continue using data: https://www.pro-football-reference.com/years/2019/passing_advanced.htm

2) *Highlight CAY/Cmp for the top 30 QB* (**N2:N32**); *control and highlight using CTRL-YAC/Cmp for top 30 QB* (**Q2:Q32**)

3) **Insert – Chart – 2-D Bar – Stacked Bar**

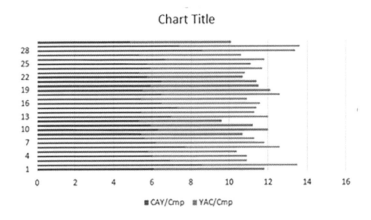

4) Chart Tools – Data - Select Data – Horizontal (Category) Axis Labels – edit – *highlight Player column to row 32* (B3:B32)

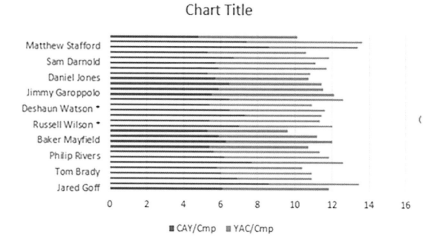

5) *Add a Descriptive Title*

6) Let's change color – *click on chart* – then on upper right *click on paintbrush* (Chart Styles) – go to **Color** – then **Colorful subcategory** – *choose 4th one down for green/blue*

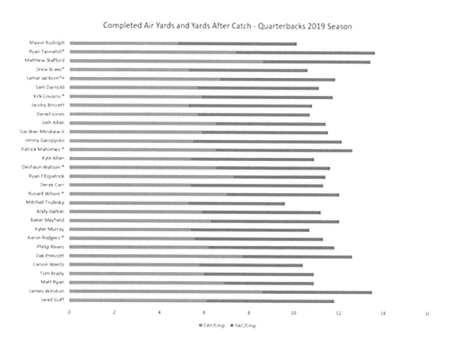

Context:

This gives the results in terms of yardage. You can see which quarterbacks had more completed air yards per completion (more of the yardage in the air) or had more yards after catch per completion (receiver running with the ball after the catch). Although this chart gives the sum of both, which is nice as it gives the average completion for each quarterback and how it was attained, this chart could also be nicely served by a percentage split between CAY/Cmp and YAC/Cmp. Although it will not show the average length of the overall average completion, it will show more clearly which quarterbacks had more than 50% of the yardage in the air as opposed to yards after the catch. To change to this chart:

7) **Chart Tools** – Design – Change Chart Type – Go to 3rd Chart in – 100% Stacked Bar

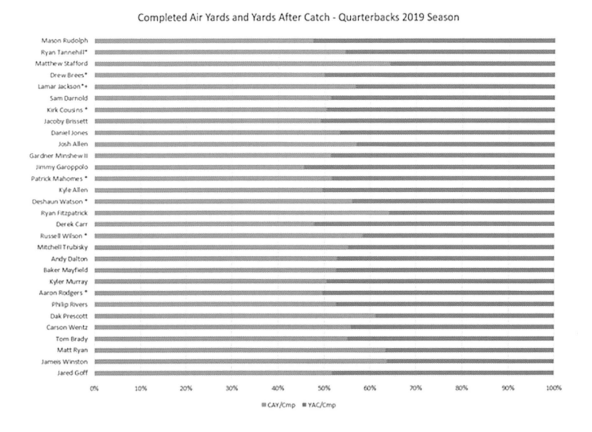

Context:

You can see that Winston, Ryan, Fitzpatrick, and Stafford all had considerably more overall yardage in the air per completion than the other quarterbacks in the sample. In their respective offenses, the quarterback threw the ball deeper down the field and the receivers were less responsible for the overall yardage after the catch. What questions can we ask here? How did these QBs (and offensive coordinators) use running backs catching the ball out of the backfield? Was it considerably different from other teams? Why did some receivers have more success than others after the catch? Is it due to breaking tackles?

In the opposite direction Jimmy Garoppolo of San Francisco had the least CAY/Cmp percentage. How did the SF offense differ in terms of use of running backs out of the backfield or in terms of screens and short passes? Again, once we start down a path, you can begin to develop additional questions to try to answer. Once you can, you can start to put everything together in terms of a story.

Moving Forward: Suggested Story Telling with Data to Pursue:

1) What QBs were under the most pressure in 2019? (Use Data from Pressure Tab in Advanced Passing. See who had most hurries, hits, and sacks)

2) Which QBs used play action the most often? Who was the most successful in play action? (Use Data form Play Type)

3) How different was the passing game in New Orleans with Brees at QB vs. Bridgewater at QB? (Use Data from any of the available Advanced Passing Tabs)

CHAPTER 6

RUSHING — BASIC STATISTICS

easures of center (location) describe the first moment of a distribution of data. While important, other dimensions are also informative, although not typically given as much attention, in particular as it relates to statistics in sports. The second moment of the distribution is known as <u>spread</u>, <u>variability</u>, or <u>dispersion</u>. <u>Spread measures the degree to which the data in a sample are tightly clustered or widely dispersed</u>. For virtually any type of statistical analysis, variability is pivotal. Statisticians who measure dispersion routinely use variability to distinguish random from non-random events, find ways to reduce it, and make decisions based upon its value.

There are a variety of measures of variability available. <u>Variance</u> is a key measure of dispersion and is calculated by taking the sum of squared deviations from the mean divided by the number of observations (n) minus 1 (n-1). It sometimes is called by an alternate name, the <u>mean-squared-error</u>. The formula for variance in a sample is below:

$$s^2 = \frac{\Sigma(x - \bar{x})^2}{n - 1}$$

The denominator may be confusing as you may expect to divide by the overall number of observations in the sample (n) rather than (n-1). We divide by (n-1) when calculating the variance as there are only (n-1) independent datapoints. Why? If we know the mean of the sample and you know (n-1) of the values in the data set, you also know the nth datapoint.

For those seeing variance for the first time, it is sometimes confusing to think about why the difference between the individual datapoints and the mean are squared. Remember, datapoints will lie both above and below the mean, so some differences will be negative and some will be positive. When we sum these values, it could be close to zero (they could cancel each other out) even though there could be a wide distribution. To overcome this shortcoming, the squared term treats values above and below the mean equally and gives us a true picture of dispersion.

One issue with variance is that the units are now in square units, not in the original units expressed in the data set. To deal with this, the square root of the variance is often displayed. The <u>square root of the variance is called the standard deviation</u>. The formula for <u>standard deviation</u> in a sample is shown below:

$$s = \sqrt{\frac{\sum(x - \bar{x})^2}{n - 1}}$$

There are three key properties of a standard deviation that are worth emphasizing when it comes to describing the variability of a distribution. First, the standard deviation is independent of the mean. In other words, it does not matter what the actual value of the mean is, it just measures how far the datapoints are from the mean. Second, standard deviation reveals the spread of a distribution. For two samples with the same mean, the one with the larger standard deviation has greater dispersion. Third, the standard deviation is independent of the number of observations in the sample. The standard deviation does not become larger just because we add more observations as it simply takes the square root of the average squared differences from the mean.

Standard deviation is not robust. As each observation takes its distance from the mean, an outlier will lie further away from the mean and will have a substantial impact on its value. One way to get a robust (resistant) measure of variability is through the <u>median absolute deviation from the median (MAD)</u>. <u>The median absolute deviation is calculated by first</u>

obtaining the median and then calculating the absolute value of the difference between the median and each observation. From this set of numbers, you then take the median to obtain the median absolute deviation. Given its use of the median, which itself is robust, MAD is not influenced by outliers and is a resistant statistic.

The range is another measure of variability. To compute the range, one simply takes the minimum value (low) and subtracts it from the maximum value (high) in the sample. This is a possible measure of variability, but it can be improved upon. The range simply states the difference between the highest and lowest values. An interquartile range, on the other hand, can be helpful in describing variability of a distribution as it notes how far from the center the data lie.

An interquartile range is calculated by first calculating the quartiles of the data distribution. The median is middle of the distribution and divides it in two. Quartiles are computed by taking the median of the upper-half of the data set and the lower-half of the data set. The median of the upper half of the data set is often referred to as Q3 (in the 75th percentile) and the median of the lower-half of the distribution is referred to as Q1 (in the 25th percentile). The median of the overall sample is Q2. The interquartile range is calculated by taking Q3 minus Q1 (Q3-Q1). This calculation of variability can be preferred to standard deviation as it avoids the sensitivity to outliers. The term percentile is introduced above. A percentile is calculated in that the Pth percentile is a value such that at least P percent of the values take on this value or less (at least (100-P) percent take on this value or more).

To explore some elements of dispersion of a data set and to visualize it in charts, let's use the basic rushing data from *Pro Football Reference*, which is available at: https://www.pro-football-reference.com/years/2019/rushing.htm.

The basic rushing statistics provided on *Pro Football Reference* are pretty straightforward. After providing the player's name, team, age, and position, it notes the following for the 2019 season:

- G – Games Played

- GS – Games Started

- Att – Rushing Attempts

- Yds – Rushing Yards

- TD – Rushing Touchdowns

- 1D – First downs gained

- Lng – Yardage of longest rush of the season

- Y/A – Rushing Yards per rushing attempt

- Y/G – Rushing Yards per game played

- Fmb – Fumbles – both lost (recovered by other team) and recovered (by runner or runner's teammate)

Context:

Rushing statistics are pretty easy to digest on the basic level. Games, attempts, yards, and touchdowns are straightforward and are similar to what we observed with quarterbacks. Same thing with ratios of yards to attempts and to games played. 1D might not immediately be obvious when you first view it, but it stands for first downs. Gaining a first down is a big deal in football as it earns another set of downs and keeps the offense on the field, increasing the probability of scoring. The 1D statistic includes any run for a first down, whether it be a first and 10 run that gains 12 or a 4th and 1 that barely made the necessary yardage. A high first down to attempts ratio likely indicates a short yardage specialist, who could be a fullback or possibly a quarterback that does not typically run in their offense. Fumbles are also shown and present a serious problem for running backs. Fumbles are counted against running backs whether they are recovered by the opposing team or not. This is due to the somewhat random outcome of which team recovers the ball. Some running backs are lucky in the sense they fumble, but they themselves or one of their teammates recovers the ball. Past results have shown that the team recovering a fumble is similar to a coin toss, so fumbles are treated the same whether the offense retains possession or not.

To do some calculations of dispersion in Excel, follow the steps below.

1) Export Data to Excel from: https://www.pro-football-reference.com/years/2019/rushing.htm

2) Eliminate 1st Row – highlight Row 1 – Home – Cells – Delete (down arrow) – Delete Rows (headers now appear in 1st Row)

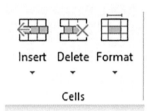

3) Freeze Panes by going to View – Freeze Panes – Freeze Top Row

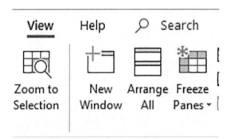

4) For this example, let's only keep the top 31 rushers in the 2019 Season – so highlight and delete all rows below row 32 –highlight row 33 and down – hit Delete - Our sample now becomes the top 31 rushers of 2019

5) Let's compute a variety of summary statistics in terms of the spread of the distribution for this sample (before doing, expand the columns a bit by

highlighting columns F through O and putting cursor at right end of cell – clicking and dragging to make them a bit wider)

  a) in h34 type =var(h2:h32)

  b) in h35 type =stdev(h2:h32)

  c) in h36 type =max(h2:h32)

  d) in h37 type =min(h2:h32)

6) Highlight all 4 cells (H34:h37) and copy – paste to I34:O37 to see all summary stats for listed variables

7) To remind yourself of which one is which, label P34:p37 as Variance, Standard Deviation, Max, Min

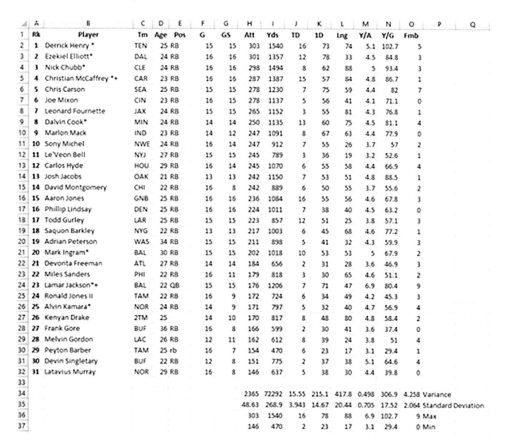

Discussion:

The quick table we created shows the variance and standard deviation of each statistic. As would be expected, these values are much higher for Yds (Yards) than they are for TD (touchdowns) and Fmb (Fumbles). Also, the Max (maximum) and Min (minimum) of each series in the sample is shown. TD's, for example, ranged from 16 (Derrick Henry – TEN) to 2 (Devin Singletary – BUF) of the top 31 rushers in terms of attempts. Fumbles are quite interesting with one rusher not fumbling at all on the season (Latavius Murray – NOR in 146 attempts) and one fumbling 9 times (quarterback Lamar Jackson – BAL in 176 attempts).

Now, let's create a chart to show dispersion. We'll begin by creating a histogram.

Histogram

1) *Highlight I1:I32* (Yds Rushing for the top 31 rushers by attempt)

2) Insert – Chart – Insert Statistics Chart (middle box directly above "Charts") – Click on Histogram

Charts

3) It automatically creates bins of 300 yards – notes the number of rushers in each bin (470-770, 770-1070, etc.)

4) Add Chart Element – Axis Titles – click on both Vertical and Horizontal – double click where axis title appears and label

5) *Add Descriptive Title*

6) Add Chart Element – Data Labels – Outside End (since the number appears here – let's eliminate the vertical axis numbers – go to Add Chart Element – Axes – undo Primary Vertical)

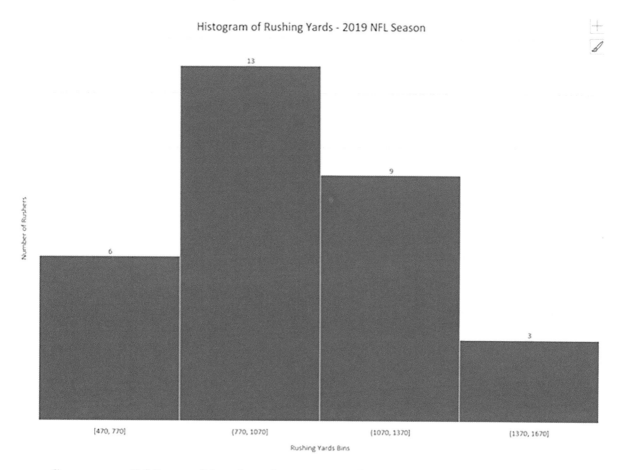

Histogram of Rushing Yards - 2019 NFL Season

Summary – Of the top 31 rushers by attempts, the most common overall yardage was 770-1070 with 13. Only 3 rushers (Henry, Chubb, and McCaffrey) had 1370+ yards on the season.

Let's compare this to Rushing Yards per Attempt (Y/A) for the same group of 31 backs (follow the same steps as above but highlight M1:M32 and adjust labels accordingly (and change color to green):

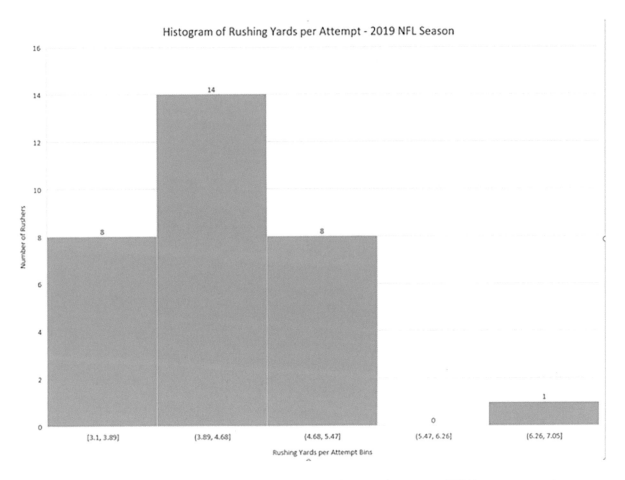

Summary – When observing Rushing Yards per Attempt (Y/A), you see the most common bin of average yards per rush was between 3.89-4.68 in the automatically defined bins with 14 rushers of the 30. 8 rushers each were in the 3.1-3.89 and 4.68-5.47 bins. No rushers averaged between 5.47 and 6.26 per carry, while one rusher had a much higher average and landed in the far right bin (quarterback Lamar Jackson who averaged 6.9 yards per attempt). Perhaps you do not like this bin size. It can be changed:

To Change Bin Size:

1) Double Click on Horizontal Axis – ***Format Axis*** – go to column bars (3rd icon under Axis Options on right-hand side menu) – click on Number of bins and change to 4

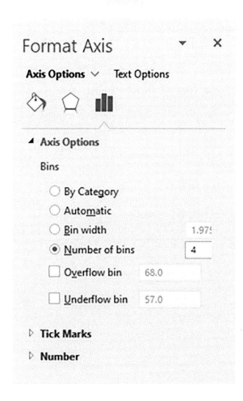

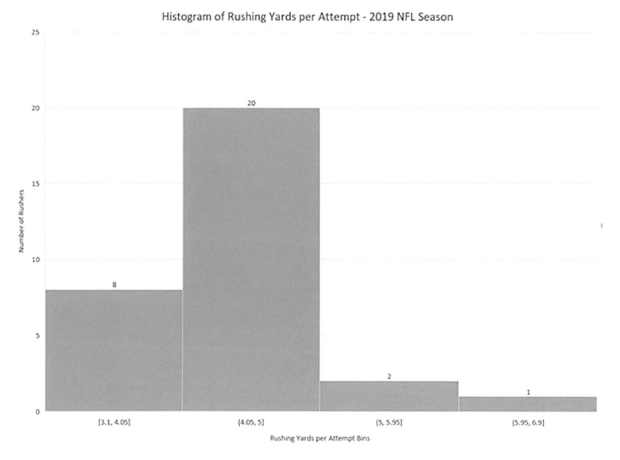

Histogram of Rushing Yards per Attempt - 2019 NFL Season

Alternatively, you could change by bin width (try 0.5 and 1.0) or any of the other options listed.

Another chart which helps to describe spread is a box and whisker plot. In a box and whisker plot you are visually presented with the full range of data. It helps to describe the distribution, both in terms of its location and also in terms of its variability. We'll create a box and whisker plot starting with touchdowns (TD) for our sample of the top 31 RB by attempts.

Box and Whiskers Plot

1) Highlight J1:J32

2) Insert – Chart – Insert Statistic Chart (middle box above Charts) – Box and Whisker Plot

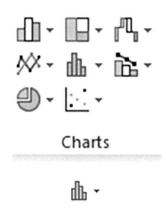

Charts

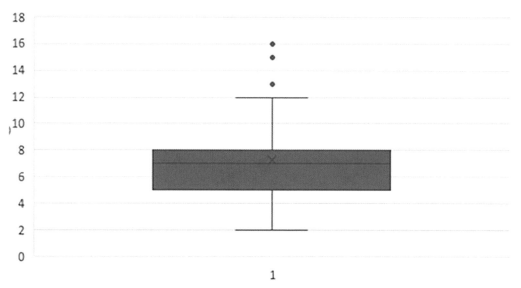

3) *Add vertical axis titles* (Add Chart Element – Axis Titles – Primary Vertical), *remove horizontal axis* (from Add Chart Element – Axes – uncheck Horizontal Axis) and *add descriptive chart title*

4) *Change color* – (right click on graph – go to ***paintbrush*** – change to yellow)

5) Add Chart Element – Data Labels – **Right**

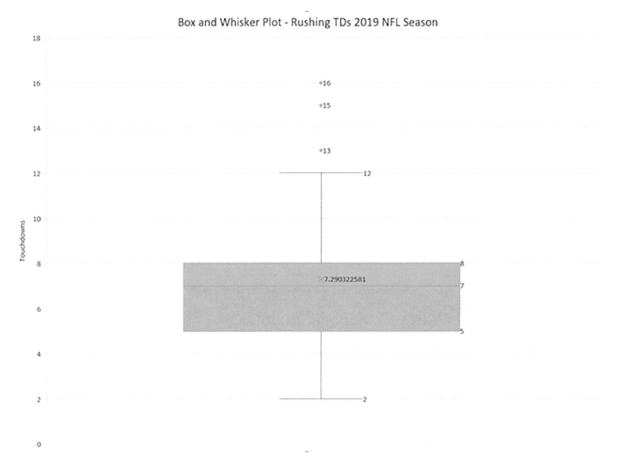

A box and whisker plot provides information across the entire distribution. The minimum is seen at the bottom (2). Going vertically, in order, the lower quartile is noted first (bottom of box (5)), the median is the line across the middle of the box (7), the mean is noted with an X (7.290322581), the upper quartile forms the top of the box (8), the maximum, excluding outliers is noted by the end of the whisker (12) and the outliers are shown (13, 15, 16).

Remember the median is where half of the sample is greater than this value (and half is less than this value). The lower quartile signifies where a quarter of the sample is less than this value, while the upper quartile notes where a quarter of the sample lies above this value. The minimum and maximum values exclude outliers, where an outlier is defined as values more (less) than 1.5 times the upper (lower) quartile.

The box and whisker plot illustrate how extraordinary the rushing TD totals of Henry, McCaffrey, and Cook were in comparison to the top rushers in the NFL for the 2019 season. Whereas the mean and median were relatively close (7 vs. approximately 7.3), the chart shows the distribution of rushing touchdowns was such that the difference between the median and lower quartile was greater than the difference between the upper quartile and the median (in terms of the number of touchdowns scored).

Let's quickly do another example following the same steps, but this time for Y/G, yards per game. After repeating the steps and changing the title accordingly:

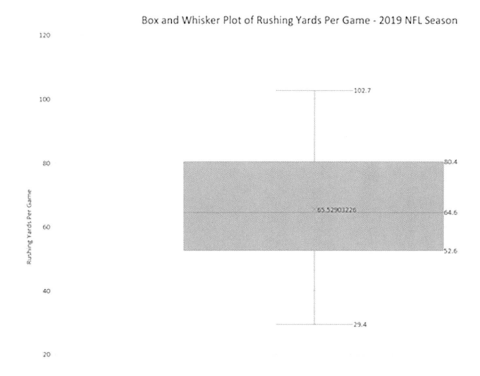

Box and Whisker Plot of Rushing Yards Per Game - 2019 NFL Season

For rushing yards per game, we first see there were no outliers in the sample. The mean and median are close (65.5 vs 64.6) and the upper part of the box is slightly larger than the lower part (differences between median and upper/lower quartile marks).

Audible: The special case of Lamar Jackson – A combination of passing and rushing data in a Radar Chart

Lamar Jackson was the MVP of the 2019 NFL season. He led Baltimore to the top record in the NFL in the regular season through his extraordinary abilities with both his arm and his feet. To illustrate his statistics on both the passing and rushing front, we first will download his gamelog from *Pro Football Reference*. A gamelog is a game-by-game data summary of his performance against each opponent in a season. Jackson's gamelog for 2019 is available here:

https://www.pro-football-reference.com/players/J/JackLa00/gamelog/2019/.

Export the data from "Share & more" – Get as Excel Workbook. Download into Excel and delete the last row (as we will not be using the season total here).

Since we will be using the yards gained in both passing and rushing, we need to relabel the columns N (Passing Yards) and W (Rushing Yards). Relabel cells N2 and W2 "Passing Yards" and "Rushing Yards", respectively. We are going to use these two columns, N and W, to make a visualization called a Radar Chart. Follow these steps:

1) Highlight N2:N17 then control-highlight W2:W17

2) Insert – Charts – Waterfall, Funnel, Stock, Surface, and Radar Charts (Above Charts – top right-hand box) – use the 3rd option from left – Filled Radar Chart

3) Change the game number (around the edge of the radar) to the opponent by going to Select Data – Horizontal (Category) Axis Labels – Edit – *highlight H3:H17* (you may need to switch over to the worksheet tab when new window appears to *highlight H3:H17*).

4) Move the Legend to the bottom by using Add Chart Element – Legend – Bottom

5) Add a descriptive title

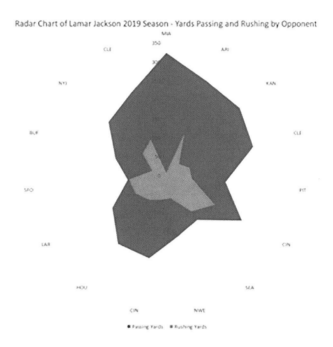

Summary:

You can see the impressive nature of Jackson's passing and rushing per game in this chart shaped like a radar. The blue area is his passing yards and the orange is his rushing yards. You can easily identify games where he threw for a high yardage total without accumulating many rushing yards (i.e. Miami) and games where his overall yardage was equally split between passing and rushing (i.e. San Francisco). The area covers the yardage gained (labeled vertically from the origin in circles – hence the radar name) and the difference in color gives insights into the two separate totals for each game.

Moving Forward: Suggested Story Telling with Data to Pursue:

1) Show the variability of 1st Downs and Long Runs for Rushers in the 2019 season.

2) Use data from the 2019 Gamelog of Derrick Henry to illustrate his performance across the entire season.

3) Compare any two backs from the same team and compare their performance in 2019 (as they both were generally rushing behind the same offensive line).

CHAPTER 7

RUSHING – ADVANCED STATISTICS

The advanced statistics on *Pro Football Reference* for rushing includes some of the same information as the basic rushing stats, but then expands into statistics which may help to distinguish how much of the success/failure of the rush actually stemmed from the running back and how much from the blockers in front of him. The key stats added to rushing on the advanced page are:

- YBC – Yards Before Contact – the sum of yardage gained before first contact with a defensive player

- YBC/Att – Yards Before Contact per attempt

- YAC – Yards After Contact – the sum of yardage gained after first contact with a defensive player

- YAC/Att – Yards After Contact per attempt

- BrkTkl – number of broken tackles on rushing plays

- Att/Br – rush attempts per broken tackles

Context:

Yards before and after contact are useful stats to attempt to disseminate rusher ability versus the abilities of blockers (offensive line, tight end(s), wide receiver(s), full back). A rusher who accumulates vast yardage before first contact with a defender is typically the beneficiary of great blocking and play design (coaching). The runner's natural abilities play a role here as well, as a well-timed juke or spin could avoid a defender, but we would typically think about high YBC running backs as the beneficiaries of terrific blocking and/or scheme. Yards after contact, on the other hand, gives insight into the rusher's natural strength and ability to continue gaining yardage after contact from a defender. High YAC numbers typically are associated with strong running backs who not only break tackles, but continue to move (or fall) forward when being wrapped up by a defender (or defenders). Being able to fall forward, rather than being stonewalled or pushed back, can be the difference between first downs and punting, and contributes greatly to team success. Broken tackles specifically accounts for the number of times a rusher broke a tackle (which could be due to poor tackling on the part of the defense or great strength/skill from the back himself) and the ratio of attempts per broken tackles puts this number in perspective compared to the number of times the back carried the ball.

The advanced rushing statistics for the 2019 NFL Season are available through *Pro Football Reference* here:

https://www.pro-football-reference.com/years/2019/rushing_advanced.htm.

Let's use this data to review bar charts, from the chapter on quarterbacks, and then construct another box and whisker plot to further explore variability of a statistic.

Two interesting and important statistics available on the advanced rushing statistics are related to first contact with a rusher. To illustrate how the most-used running backs fared in terms of Yardage Before and After Contact, we'll construct two charts using the top 10 rushers in terms of attempts on the 2019 season. First, we'll return to horizontal bar charts to create a 2-D clustered bar chart. To begin:

1) Delete first row. There should now only be one header row.

2) *Highlight L1:L11* to get the top 10 rushers (in terms of attempts) Yards Before Contact divided by Attempts (YBC/Att).

3) *CTRL-Highlight N1:N11* to also get Yards After Contact divided by Attempts (YAC/Att) for the same group of backs.

4) Insert – Charts – 2-D Bar – Clustered Bar

5) Select Data – Horizontal (Category) Axis Labels – Edit – B2:B11 (to get rushers' names)

6) *Add a Descriptive Title*

Yards Before and After Contact - Rushers - 2019 NFL Season

Context:

In the group of top 10 rushers (by attempts) for the 2019 season, a few interesting results are immediately seen on the chart. First, Derek Henry, Nick Chubb, and Leonard Fournette were all very good (possibly great) after first contact. Henry rushed for an additional 3+ yards per attempt after first being hit by a defensive player. Fournette and Chubb were not very far behind. On the other hand, Christian McCaffrey, Marlon Mack, and Ezekiel Elliot each had the highest averages of Yards Before Contact (highlighting the skills of both the blockers in front of them and their own skills), with varying degrees of success in terms of Yards After Contact, of this subset of players in our sample.

Although this is useful information, it may also be quite informative to illustrate the ratio of Yards Before Contact to Yards After Contact, instead of the viewer of the chart needing to try to do this in his or her head. We have the means already to do this through the use of a 100% Stacked Bar Chart. If you would like, you could re-create the steps listed above and then opt for the 100% Stacked Bar Chart instead of the 2-D Clustered Bar Chart. A quicker option is just to follow these steps to change the chart from its current output:

1) Click anywhere on your chart

2) **Chart Tools** – Design – Change Chart Type (right-middle of the upper part of the screen – to the right of the Data section and to the left of the Location section)

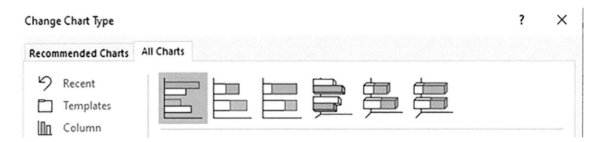

3) Change to Bar – 100% Stacked Bar (3ʳᵈ chart in from left)

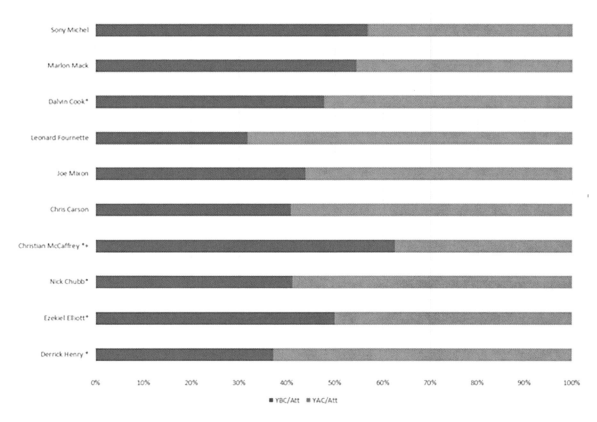

Through the use of the 100% Stacked Bar Chart, it is straightforward to see how important Yards Before Contact was to Christian McCaffrey's season and how Leonard Fournette and Derrick Henry dominated after first contact. These stats shed some insight into how injuries to an offensive line may be more important to McCaffrey's success on rushing plays than it might be to Henry or Fournette (similar questions could be posed for New England and Indianapolis in terms of Sony Michel and Marlon Mack). Likewise, it begs the question of if the Yards Before Contact per Attempt average for Fournette is due to poor line play (whereas if the line improved, it makes Fournette even more valuable) or if this has more to do with vision and first step on the part of Fournette himself.

Another interesting statistic available on the advanced rushing section of *Pro Football Reference* is Broken Tackles. How did our top ten rushers (in terms of attempts) fare in terms of breaking tackles? To put on a more equal scale with each other, let's visualize the Attempts per Broken Tackle (Att/Br) variable for the top 10 backs in terms of a box and whisker plot.

1) Highlight P1:P11

2) Insert – Charts – Insert Statistics Chart – **Box and Whisker**

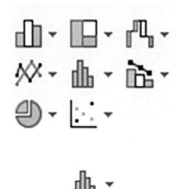

3) *Add vertical axis titles* (from Add Chart Element – Axis Titles – Primary Vertical), *remove horizontal axis* (from Add Chart Element – Axes – uncheck Horizontal Axis)

4) Change color – (right click on graph – go to ***paintbrush*** – change to green for some variety)

5) Add Chart Element – Data Labels – Right

Add Chart
Element ▾ |

6) Add Title

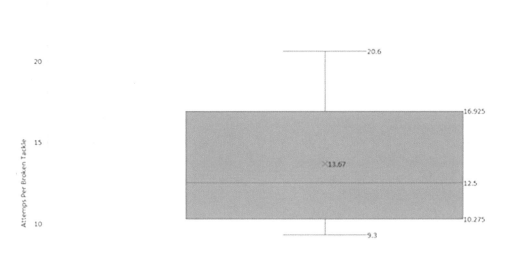

Box and Whisker of Attempts Per Broken Tackle - Rushers - 2019 NFL Season

This chart gives some insight into the distribution of this subset of the sample of rushers (top 10 in terms of attempts) where the mean is higher than the median. The max and min are shown, no outliers exist as pre-defined by the creation process of the chart in Excel, with the gap between the median and 3rd Quartile being larger than the gap between the median and 1st Quartile. With a feel for the spread of the distribution from the box and whisker plot, we can pair that with a simple 2-D Bar chart to show how each rusher in the sample fared (following same steps as earlier in the chapter and adjusting the title).

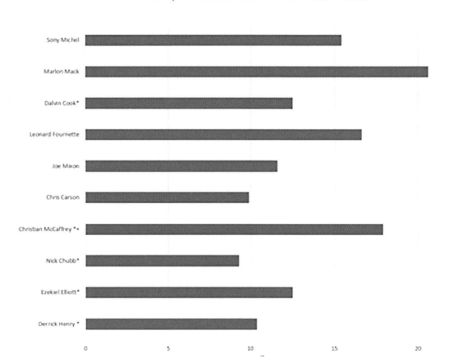

Attempts Per Broken Tackle - Rushers - 2019 NFL Season

For the given sample, we see it took the most rushing attempts to have a broken tackle for Marlon Mack, while it took the fewest for Nick Chubb. Chris Carson and Derrick Henry also had considerable success achieving broken tackles more often as it relates to their carries.

Moving Forward: Suggested Story Telling with Data to Pursue:

1) Look at rushers from the same team and see how similar/different they perform. Use a filter to sort by team and construct charts to illustrate the types of runners on a team and how they appear to be used.

2) What is the relationship between age and attempts? Any evidence that older backs are used less frequently?

3) In terms of rushers, who gained the most first downs? What does this distribution look like across rushers?

CHAPTER 8

BASIC RECEIVING

The next set of data available for the 2019 season is on receiving. Receiving covers passes caught by anyone on the roster, most notably wide receivers, tight ends, and running backs. Standard receiving data for the 2019 season is available on *Pro Football Reference* here: https://www.pro-football-reference.com/years/2019/receiving.htm. The basic receiving statistics are similar to rushing statistics as they overlap in many cases. There are columns for yards, yards per reception, touchdowns, first downs, long reception, and fumbles that were described in the previous section on rushing. The new statistics here are noted below:

- Tgt – Targets – how many times a receiver was "targeted" – how many passes were thrown to him on season

- Rec – Receptions – how many of the passes intended for him were caught by the receiver

- Ctch% - Catch Percentage – the ratio of receptions to targets – how many balls were caught out of the number of balls thrown to the receiver

- Y/Tgt – Yards per target average

- R/G – Receptions per game average

- Y/G – Yards per game average

Context:

The basic statistics on *Pro Football Reference* for receiving include not only receptions, but the number of passes thrown to the receiver as well. This variable is called targets and it notes how many passes were intended for the receiver. This is a useful statistic as it helps to isolate how frequently the receiver was involved in the offense. Even more useful, catch percentage takes the ratio of receptions to targets to see how often the receiver caught the pass intended for him. Yards per target and receptions per game further detail these insights. Although not presented here, it is easy enough to compute the targets per game as well, to better compare receivers when they missed games due to injury, suspension, or otherwise.

The table of statistics for receivers includes all players who caught passes. This table is helpful in examining wide receivers, tight ends, and the receiving of running backs. The position is provided so it is possible to separate or filter the results to focus on a specific position. This is useful from the team perspective, but is also important if you play fantasy football.

In this chapter, we'll use the basic receiving statistics to plot one variable compared to another variable using a scatterplot. In a scatterplot we can see how two series are related. They may look like they move together, move apart, or appear quite randomly distributed. Scatterplots are straightforward to create in Excel and can provide a wide array of insights.

To begin, let's plot the relationship between Targets (Tgt) and Receptions (Rec). Targets are the number of times a receiver was thrown to, while receptions are the number of passes he caught. The success rate that the receiver catches the ball is partially dependent upon their own ability and also on the ability of the quarterback to deliver the ball (with the help of blockers). To keep the data manageable, we'll limit the chart to show the top 10 receivers on the season in terms of receptions.

To create a <u>Scatterplot</u>:

1) *Highlight H1:I11* – (highlight the header row and the 10 rows underneath it in columns H and I)

2) Insert – Chart – Insert Scatter or Bubble Chart (directly above the word "Charts" in the Charts section) – choose the first option

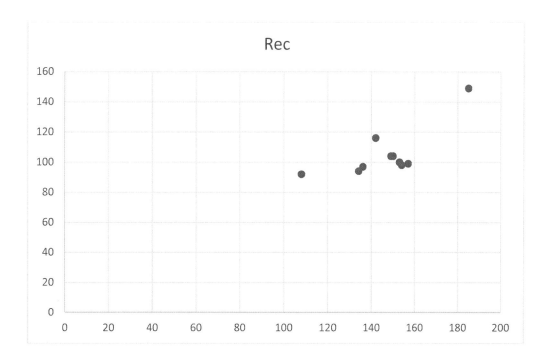

In this example, Targets are plotted on the X-axis (horizontal) and Receptions are plotted on the Y-axis (vertical). Each point represents one of the top 10 receivers on the 2019 season. Although it typically is good to leave each axis starting at zero, so the reader has an immediately identifiable starting point, let's allow more space to observe this distribution of points and change the range on which the X- and Y-axes are plotted.

3) *Click on Horizontal Axis* (box should appear around axis labels) – ***Format Axis*** appears on right-hand side of screen

4) Under Axis Options, *click on the icon of the 3 columns – click the arrow for **Axis Options** – change the Bounds – Minimum to 100*

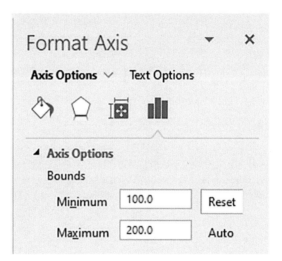

5) *Click on the Vertical Axis* (box should appear around axis labels) – ***Format Axis*** appears on right-hand side

6) Under ***Axis Options***, *click the icon of the 3 columns – click the arrow for **Axis Options** – change the Bounds – Minimum to 80*

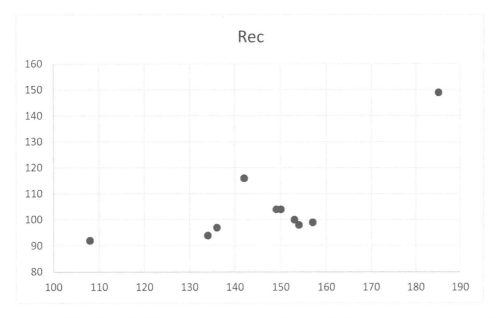

Now, let's directly label the data points (circles) with the player it corresponds to:

7) Add Chart Element – Data Labels – Below (will label with Receptions)

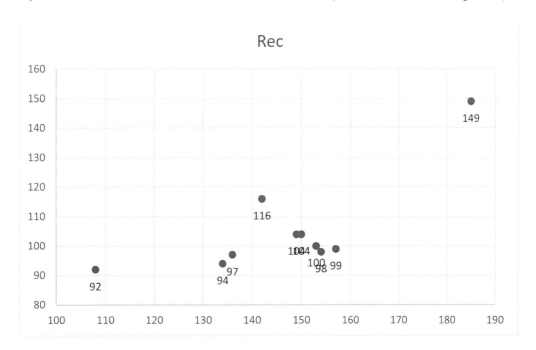

To change the numbers (Receptions) to Player Name:

8) *Click on any of the numbers under the points* – boxes will appear around each number

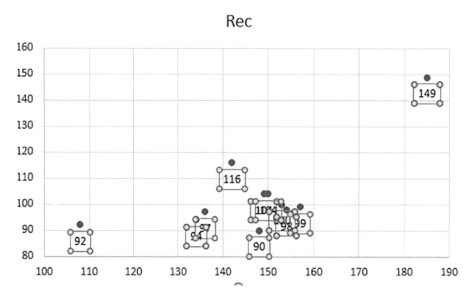

9) Add Chart Element – Data Labels – More Data Label Options – Right-hand side box will appear – *click on the 3 Bars*

10) Under ***Label Options*** – Label Contains – *check Value From Cells* – highlight B2:B11

11) *Uncheck Y Value* (currently would have player name and receptions – after unchecking just left with player name)

12) *Move chart to new sheet* – there are some overlaps in name – you can click on any name and drag to an area where you can see it – a line will show up to indicate which data point is which. (I'll move a few around so they can be seen.)

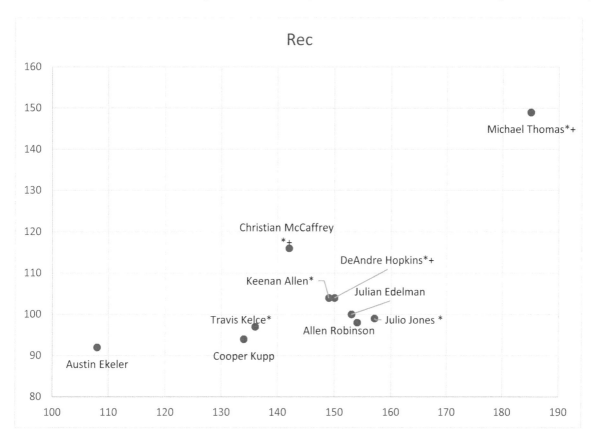

We can show the linear relationship between the data with a trendline. A trendline shows a line of best fit of the data points in our plotted sample.

To add a linear trendline:

13) Add Chart Element – Trendline – Linear

14) *Add Axis titles and a descriptive title*

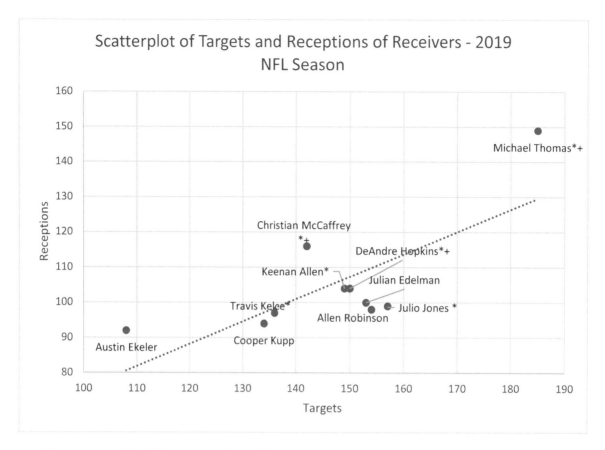

Our scatterplot illustrates a few things immediately to the viewer. First, we see what an incredible season Michael Thomas had for New Orleans compared to all the other receivers in the league. He had many more targets and receptions as is evidenced by his location in the top right corner. Christian McCaffrey had a pretty high percentage of receptions to targets, likely due to him being a running back as he received many short passes (in addition to his natural receiving ability). On the other hand, Allen Robinson, Julian Edelman, and Julio Jones had a relatively low ratio of receptions to targets among this group of receivers.

Moving Forward: Suggested Story Telling with Data to Pursue:

1) Who were the best receivers in 2019 in terms of scoring touchdowns? What players had the most/least touchdowns compared to their receptions?

2) Compare receivers from the same team and show their relative productivity.

3) Which receivers excelled at making first downs? What receivers had the most success gaining first downs compared to their overall number of receptions?

CHAPTER 9

ADVANCED RECEIVING

Advanced receiving statistics for the 2019 NFL season are available at https://www.pro-football-reference.com/years/2019/receiving_advanced.htm. The advanced statistics for receivers further expand the details on how far down the field they caught passes, their skills after the catch, and how many balls they dropped. The statistics that are on the basic receptions and those that have been described in other sections are not reiterated here, but the new relevant stats are listed below:

- YBC – Total yards the ball traveled in the air before being caught by the receiver

- YBC/R – Total yards the ball traveled in the air before being caught by the receiver divided by receptions

- YAC – Yards gained after catch

- YAC/R – Yards gained after catch divided by receptions

- ADOT – Average depth of target

- BrkTkl – Tackles broken by receiving player

- Rec/Br – Ratio of receptions to broken tackles

- Drop – Dropped Passes – Pass was on-target but did not result in a reception by receiver

- Drop% - Dropped Passes divided by Targets – percentage of passes intended for receiver that were dropped

Context:

The advanced statistics take the quarterback's side of the relationship and relates it to individual receivers. YBC is an aggregate measure of how far the quarterback threw the ball in the air before the receiver caught the pass. YBC/R is an average of this figure per reception. These statistics help to identify players who are "deep threats", who may be targeted more on passes downfield rather than on short routes. Specialists of this type will have high numbers in YBC and YBC/R. The best receivers often have a good mix of short catches and long catches, so the numbers may be more of a reflection of the type of offense, the ability of the quarterback, or quality of the quarterback protection (to allow time to throw the ball downfield) than of the receiver himself.

Receiver ability to gain yardage after the catch is highlighted by YAC and YAC/R. These figures are derived from the total yardage (and total yardage divided by receptions) gained after a receiver made the catch. Broken tackles also play a role here. So-called possession receivers often do not accumulate a great amount of yardage after the catch. These receivers tend to be valued for their skills in catching the football and may not have as much speed or agile moves as other receivers. Their route-running and hands put them in the league, and they may be used to "move the chains" on 3rd down situations by getting open immediately beyond the first down marker. Receivers with high numbers for YAC and YAC/R either break tackles to gain additional yardage (a skill that is mostly attributable to the receiver himself and/or the quality of the defender attempting to make a tackle), have the speed to create separation from defenders (thereby creating addition room to run after the catch), or are the beneficiaries of quarterbacks who can "lead" them into space to lengthen the gain on the play.

Drops are one of the worst things a receiver can do, and it often considerably impacts a drive and the ability to score or keep the clock moving (depending on game situation). A high number of drops and/or a high drop percentage can be a quick ticket out of the league for receivers.

In this chapter, let's take the scatterplot one step further by adding an additional piece of information to the chart. While the X and Y axes will be plotted as before, we'll add another dimension by making size of the points (circles) a variable as well. This type of chart is called a Bubble Chart and it is an option under the same setting where we selected a scatterplot.

Let's create our first bubble chart by using data on Yards Before Catch (YBC), Yards After Catch (YAC), and Broken Tackles (BrkTkl). These three variables are interrelated as they show how far, on the average, the ball traveled in the air before the receiver caught the ball, how many yards he ran for after the catch, and how many tackles he broke on the season (which contributes to more positive yardage after the catch). To create a bubble chart:

1) *Highlight M1:M11; CNTL-Highlight O1:O11; CNTL-Highlight R1:R11* (we'll do top 10 receivers by receptions as in the previous example)

2) Insert – Charts – Insert Scatter or Bubble Chart – Go down to Bubble and choose the first option

Charts

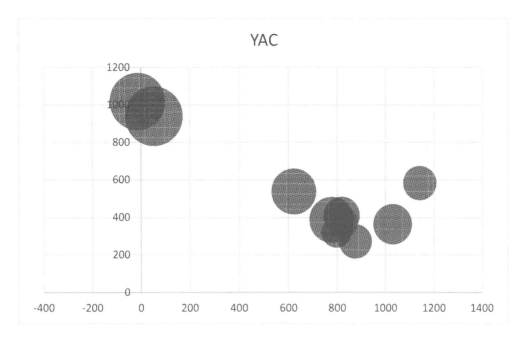

Let's make the bubbles a bit smaller, so they are easier to identify

3) *Click on any bubble – **Format Data Series** (opens on right-hand side of screen) – click on the 3 columns*

4) Go down to ***Size Represents** – click on Width of Bubbles –* change "Scale bubble size to" 25 (instead of 100)

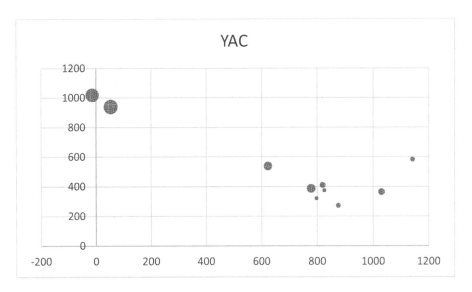

5) Add Chart Element – Data Labels – More Data Label Options – Right-hand side box will appear – click on the 3 Columns

6) Under Label Options – Label Contains – check Value From Cells – *highlight B2:B11*

7) Uncheck Y Value

8) Some labels overlap – so click and move some names to empty spaces

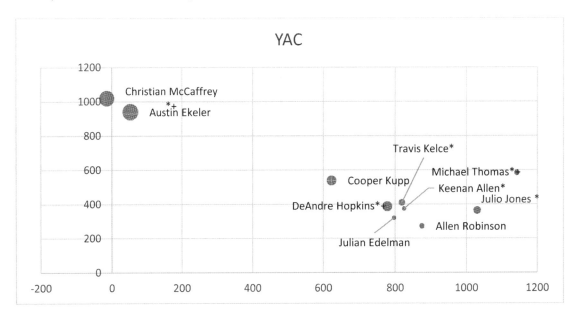

9) Add Chart Element – Trendline – Linear

10) Add Chart Element – Legend - Top

11) Add Axis titles and a descriptive title

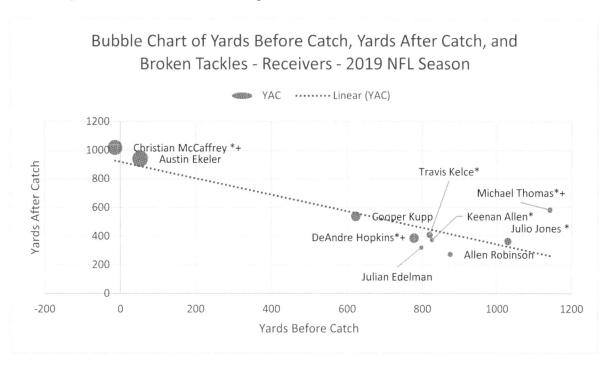

Context:

This chart brings out a few key points of insight. First, the two running backs in our sample, McCaffrey and Ekelar, are both located in the top left corner of the chart. This illustrates they had few yards before catch and many yards after catch. This makes sense for running backs as they caught many passes coming out of the backfield. In McCaffrey's case, his actual yardage before catch was negative on the season! This translates that for the majority of catches, McCaffrey was receiving the ball behind the line of scrimmage.

When we turn our attention to the rest of the sample, we notice that all the players were wide receivers other than Travis Kelce, who plays Tight End. We see some similarities as they are bunched in the same general area. The one clearly outside that bunch is Michael Thomas, who led the league in Yards Before Catch and was the highest wide receiver in Yards After Catch as well. The size of the bubbles, representing broken tackles, were dominated by the running backs, but notice the success DeAndre Hopkins and Cooper Kupp had in this category via their large circles. Julian Edelman and Keenan Allen had relatively few broken tackles as evidenced by their smaller circles.

Audible: Michael Thomas – Week-by-Week Performance 2019 Season

Michael Thomas had an incredible season in 2019. With additional data found on *Pro Football Reference*, we can look at his performance on a game-by-game level. His performance, by week, is included as a "Gamelog" and it is available on the website here: https://www.pro-football-reference.com/players/T/ThomMi05/gamelog/2019/. Import the regular season data in Excel and delete the last row (row 19) as we do not need the totals for this exercise.

We can map his performance over time using the weekly observations available in the data set. To do this we'll introduce a new chart to our arsenal, the line chart. Let's start with a simple mapping of his targets (passes thrown in his direction) and his receptions (the number of passes he caught).

To create a line chart, follow the steps below.

1) Highlight K2:L18

2) Insert – Charts – Insert Line or Area Chart (middle row of buttons above Charts on left) – use the first option simply titled Line

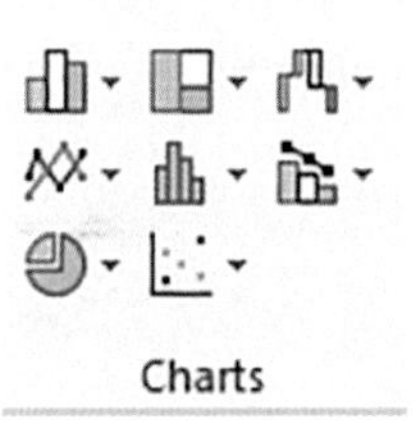

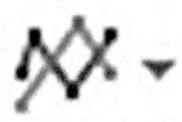

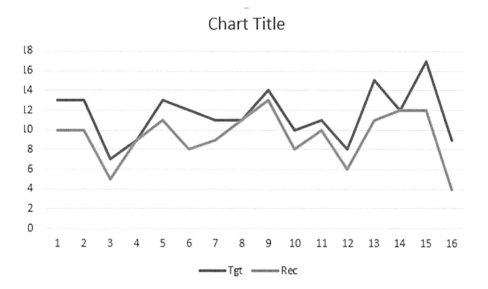

3) We can keep the horizontal axis as is and refer to it as game number or change to list the opponent or date – I'll choose date in this case – Select Data – Horizontal (Category) Axis Labels – Edit – *highlight B3:B18*

4) *Add a title*

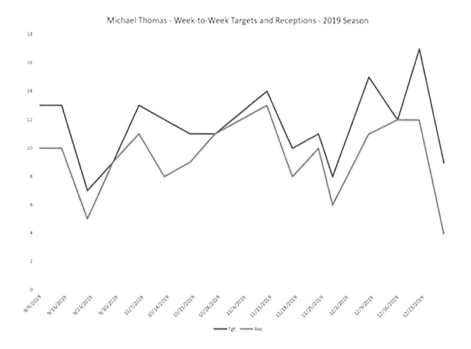

We can see how closely the receptions match the targets over the course of the season. We immediately see there were two occasions where every time he was targeted he caught the pass (9/29/19 and 10/27/20). We see the targets ebb and flow over the season with the highest season total of targets occurring in the next-to-last week of the season. His consistent stream of receptions, happening 10+ times a game on multiple occasions, are evident which led to his season-leading total by a wide margin.

To continue to explore Michael Thomas's season, we can use the area graph that is available under the same option as the line graph. This time let's create a chart of his Yards per Reception (Y/R) and Yards per Target (Y/Tgt).

1) *Highlight Q2:Q18 and CTRL-Highlight N2:N18*

2) Insert – Charts – Insert Line or Area Chart – Area Chart

3) Change horizontal Axis to Date – Select Data – Horizontal (Category) Axis Labels – *highlight B3:B18*

4) *Add a title*

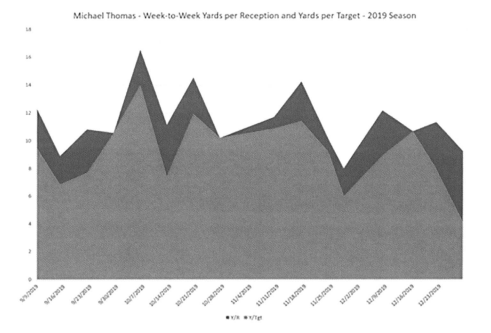

Michael Thomas - Week-to-Week Yards per Reception and Yards per Target - 2019 Season

In terms of yards per reception and target, several peaks are evident in the graph, specifically where he gained over 16 yards per reception (and 14 yards per target) on September 29th. Other big games, where he gained over 14 yards per reception, are seen as similar blue peaks on the graph. The games where he caught every pass thrown his way, as mentioned above, are also shown here as there is no blue evident above the orange for those games (as his yardage per reception equaled his yardage per target as they were one in the same). Personally, I prefer the simple lines to the areas, but there is obviously more color in the area graph to attract viewers, so the personal preference is up to you as you begin to get a feel for creating charts of football statistics in Excel.

Moving Forward: Suggested Story Telling with Data to Pursue:

1) Which receivers dropped the most passes in 2019? What was their percentage of drops?

2) What is the relationship between receiving yards and first downs? Which receivers performed well in earning first downs without large yardage totals?

3) Map out Christian McCaffrey's season game-by-game. What does his receiving performance look like? Were teams in the division more or less successful in stopping him the second time they played in 2019?

CHAPTER 10

KICKING AND PUNTING

K ickers and punters are covered, statistics-wise, on a separate page on *Pro Football Reference* which can be accessed here:

https://www.pro-football-reference.com/years/2019/kicking.htm.

There are a variety of possibilities to explore here as kickers are evaluated on field goal kicking, extra points, and kickoffs. Kicking statistics have become more detailed and this helps considerably with analysis. Punting statistics on *Pro Football Reference* are still pretty basic, but at least allow for some investigation of their performance. Descriptions of the statistical categories are noted below:

- FGA – Field Goals Attempted

- FGM – Field Goals Made

    o Both of these stats are available overall and by range 0-19, 20-29, etc.

- Lng – Long Field Goal on the season

- FG% - Field Goals Made divided by Field Goals Attempted – expressed as a percentage

- XPA – Extra Points Attempted

- XPM – Extra Points Made

- XP% - Extra Points Made divided by Extra Points Attempted – expressed as a percentage

- KO – number of Kick Offs

- KOYds – Total yards of all Kick Offs made

- TB – number of Touchbacks (kickoffs that were in bounds and not returned)

- TB% - Number of Touchbacks divided by the number of Kick Offs

- KOAvg – Kick Off Yards divided by number of Kick Offs

- Pnt – Number of Punts

- Yds – Punting Yards

- Lng – Long Punt on the season

- Blck – number of blocked punts

- Y/P – Yards per Punt

Context:

Field goal kicker statistics are listed by range first and then overall. In the past, statistics were generally only available in terms of overall field goals attempted and made. This made it difficult to compare kickers as one kicker may have been asked to kick more long field goals than others. Now, on *Pro Football Reference*, you can obtain field goals by range to see if a kicker missed only in specific ranges or had a similar overall success or failure rate across distances. Kickers without the ability to kick very long field goals typically are not asked to attempt the same number of 50+ yard field goals as others, so this too can bias any comparison.

Extra points have become more challenging since the rule change concerning Point-After-Touchdown (PAT) attempts in 2015. The extra point is now tried (if attempted rather than a two-point conversion attempt) from 33 yards from the goal post (15 yards from the goal line). This was a considerable change from a 20-yard attempt and has caused the percentage made to fall from the early 2010s success rate of 98-99%. This rule change was made to make the kick itself more competitive and exciting and also to encourage more 2-point conversion attempts. Kicker success in extra points can be seen through attempts (XPA), made (XPM), and percentage (XP%).

Another duty that place kickers have in the NFL is to kick the ball off to the opponent after a score or to start a half or overtime. Most kickers that attempt field goals for teams are also the same player who kicks off, but this is not universal as there are kick off specialists (or a punter could be a kickoff specialist as well). Kick offs are important for field position. Kick offs through the endzone or not returned out of the endzone are called touchbacks. In the event of a touchback, the offensive team starts with the ball on their own 25-yard line (prior to 2018, the offense started with the ball on their own 20). Touchbacks used to be quite valuable as the opposing team would not have had the opportunity to turn a return into a potential big play. With the new rules, however, some teams have found it possible to kick the ball higher, allowing for more time for the coverage to converge on the kick returner, to attempt to prevent the ball from being returned to the 25 (or longer) to place the opposing team in a more difficult position. Field position is very important in football and teams that face longer fields to score are generally less successful. Kick off yardage, touchbacks, touchback percentage, and Kick off Average (KOAvg) are all useful in their own right due to the possible kickoff strategies noted above and how well a team was able to implement them (i.e. if they attempted a touchback vs. tried to prevent a return to the 25 or beyond).

Punting statistics are very mundane. Number of punts, yards covered, the long on the season, the number of blocked punts, and yards per punt are shown for anyone who made a punt in the 2019 season. Generally, punters who punt the ball greater distances are more valuable, however, there are various caveats to this rule. Some kickers are very good at punting the ball so that it goes out of bounds, is fair caught (receiver/returner of punt gives up the right to run with the ball after the catch as to not be hit and be able to catch the ball – to prevent further yardage on the punt after it hits the ground), or simply stops before the goal line (often with backspin – like in golf). Given that all punts are counted equal in the stats presented here, we cannot distinguish those situations and would need play-by-play data to better analyze punter effectiveness. In addition, blocks may not fully be attributable to the punter himself. It could be due to a bad snap (long snapper), poor protection (line), opposing special teams rush ability (other team), or slow mechanics (punter).

To work with this data a bit more effectively, let's sort the data to obtain some subsets that we want to visualize. Download the data from https://www.pro-football-reference.com/years/2019/kicking.htm. The first row of data, once you bring it into Excel, is headers that break the statistics into different categories. Instead of re-labeling all of the 2nd row to correspond to the first (which I recommend if you want to work with the field goal ranges, for instance), let's highlight the second row by clicking on the gray 2 on row 2 so that the whole row is highlighted. Now, go up top to Data and then look for Sort & Filter on the ribbon. Click Filter (big filter icon) in the Sort and Filter section and drop-down arrows are now available for each column.

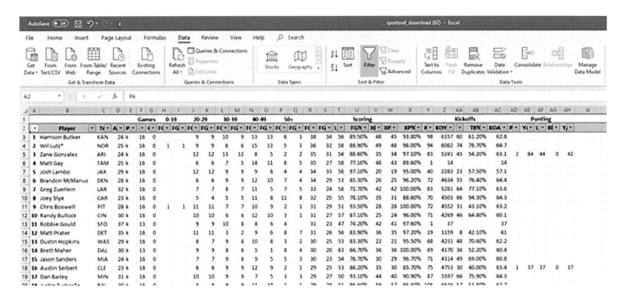

Let's focus on kickoffs first (they start the game after all), and let's use the down arrow in column Y to sort from largest to smallest. Once you click on the down arrow, the new window appears. Click Sort Largest to Smallest (2nd option down). Now the data set is sorted by number of kickoffs, from largest to smallest with Justin Tucker of Baltimore leading the way on the 2019 season with 106 kickoffs.

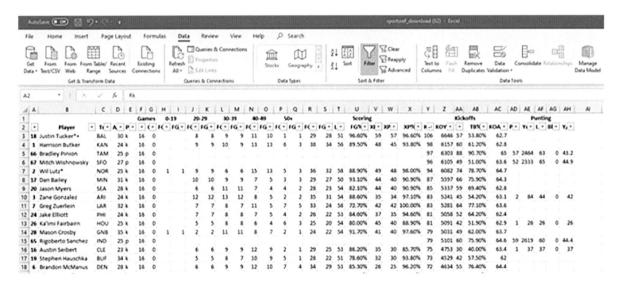

Let's use this data to make a <u>combination chart</u>. A combination chart uses two different charts in one setting. One advantage to this approach is saving space, as all elements are in one chart, but another advantage is to map out two things of which we have interest, but are measured on different scales. Let's explore this type of chart using touchback percentage (TB%) and Kickoff Average (KOAvg) for the kickers with the 10 most kickoffs in the 2019 season (this is how we already have it sorted). Follow the steps below.

1) *Highlight AB2:AC11*

2) Insert – Charts – Insert Combo Chart – Use first option Clustered Column-Line

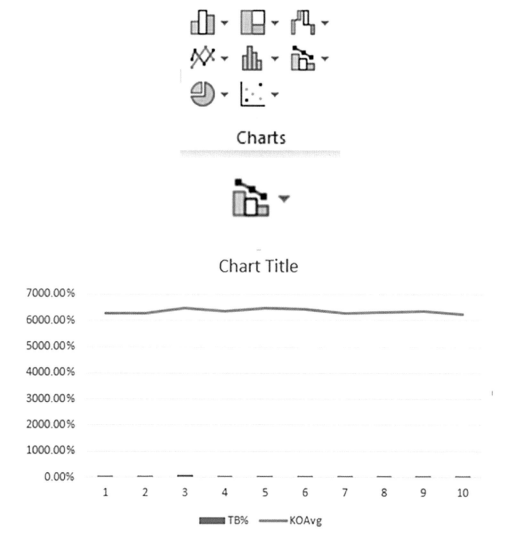

In the way this is plotted, it is not useful as there is no rhyme or reason to the chart. However, this point is not our end goal. The goal is to add a secondary axis and plot these on the same chart.

3) In Ribbon, Go to Type – Change Chart Type (new window opens)

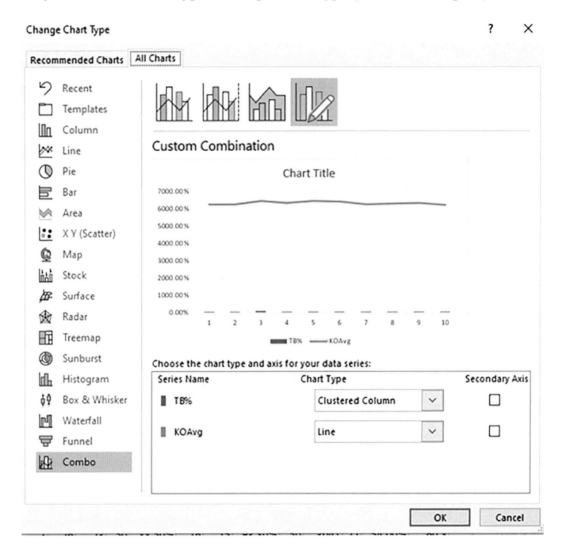

4) Check the Secondary Axis box in the KOAvg row

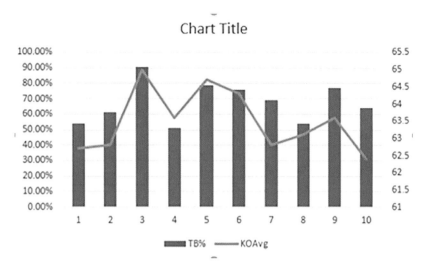

This looks more promising as the TB% is a column and KOAvg is a line. The touchback percentage is noted on the left, while the Kickoff average is noted on the right. This needs to be described, so we need to label the Axes, put the kicker names on the horizontal axis, then give a title to the chart.

5) Add Chart Element – Axis Titles – Primary Vertical (click where title appears and name)

6) Add Chart Element – Axis Titles – Secondary Vertical (click where title appears and name)

7) Data – Select Data – Horizontal (Category) Axis Labels – Edit – *Highlight B3:B12*

8) *Add Descriptive Chart Title*

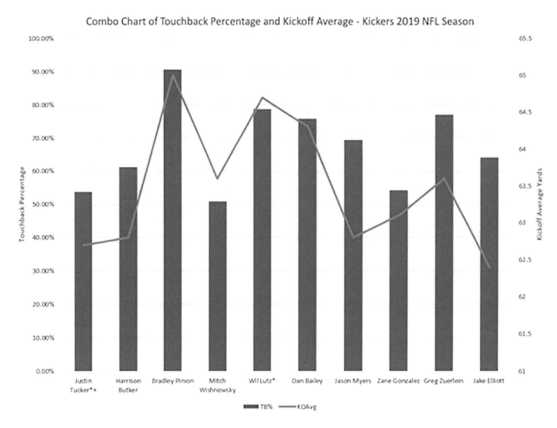

Combo Chart of Touchback Percentage and Kickoff Average - Kickers 2019 NFL Season

We can see that Bradley Pinion led the group in both touchback percentage and kickoff average playing half of his games in the thin air a mile high in Denver, Colorado. Mitch Wishnowsky had the lowest touchback percentage of the group, combined with a middle-of-the-pack kickoff average. The top kicker in the number of kickoffs on the season, Justin Tucker, was relatively low in terms of both touchback percentage and kickoff average.

Although Tucker may not have dominated in the two categories listed above, he did have a very good season for Baltimore in 2019. How did Tucker fare in field goals made by distance? To summarize this information, let's explore the use of a pie chart. We'll use the field goals made (FGM) for each range he had made field goals, which were 20-29, 30-39, 40-49, and 50+.

1) *Highlight K2:K3, then CTRL-highlight M2:M3, O2:O3, and Q2:Q3*

2) Insert – Charts – 2-D Pie (lower left in this area)

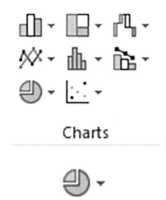

Charts

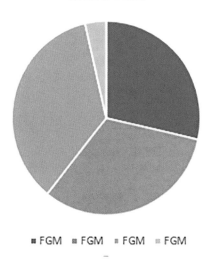

3) Select Data – Horizontal (Category) Axis Labels – Edit – Highlight box with 20-29 (it's combined but looks like J and K in row 1), CNTL-highlight 30-39 in row 1, CNTL-highlight 40-49 in row 1, and CNTL-highlight 50+ in row 1

4) Add Chart Element – Data Labels – Inside End

5) *Add Title*

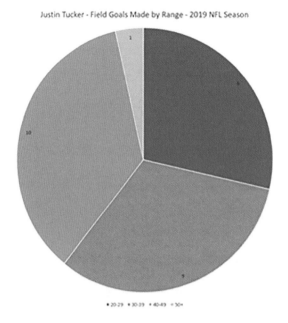

Justin Tucker - Field Goals Made by Range - 2019 NFL Season

The pie chart breaks each category into pieces of a pie, with the size of the slice representing how many in each part. Tucker only had 1 field goal made from 50+ yards and this can be seen with the thin slice in yellow. He made the most field goals between 40-49 yards with 10, represented by the gray piece of the pie.

Many people that use charts and graphs have the same reaction to a pie chart which is similar to what happens when you tell a Philadelphia Eagles fan that you are a fan of the Dallas Cowboys. In short, it's not pretty. There is often much distain and anger. Many people hate pie charts for some of the reasons you see here. At first glance, without reading the data labels, it may be tough to determine which slice of the pie is bigger, the gray, orange, or blue areas. They are all close, but Tucker made more field goals from 40-49 (10) compared to 30-39 (9) and 20-29 (8). The data labels clarify this, but at first glance this could be troubling to the viewer. Although pie charts are met with intense dislike, they are still covered in testing for the SAT and ACT and are worth exploring. Although there are likely better ways to show the results in other charts, pie charts can still be colorful options to illustrate general points, particularly if the exact details are not pivotal to the story you are trying to tell or are explored in complementary charts presented with the pie chart.

Moving Forward: Suggested Story Telling with Data to Pursue:

1) Which Kickers attempted the most 50+ yard field goals? Who was most successful?

2) Use a combination chart to show how closely related Field Goal Percentage is to Extra Point Percentage for the top kickers.

3) Which punters had the most punts in the 2019 season? How did they fare in terms of Yards per Punt?

CHAPTER 11

BASIC DEFENSE

Defensive stats available to the public were long overdue for the game of football. In any sport, defense is typically more difficult to measure than offense, but for the longest time only very simple statistics were available for players on defense. When I was growing up a way to learn about players was through football cards. Defensive players typically did not get as many cards in a card set as offensive players and, in the cases they did, the back of their card included a "write-up" on the player (words) as opposed to stats (numbers) which dominated the back of offensive player cards.

Pro Football Reference has some very good defensive stats listed on their basic defense page, which span across the different positions on the defensive side of the ball. After giving the basic player information (name, team, age, position, games, games started), the website gives information about Interceptions, Fumbles, and Tackles. The key stats in each category are described below:

Interceptions

- Int – Interceptions – when a pass by a quarterback is "picked off" by a defensive player, resulting in a change in possession

- Yds – Yardage gained after the interception

- TD – touchdowns as a result of interceptions

- Lng – longest interception return

- PD – Passes Defended – when a defensive player effectively defends a pass in his direction through deflection of the football or a simultaneous hit on a receiver when the ball arrived

Fumbles:

- FF – Forced Fumbles – player forced a fumble – could have been recovered by either team

- Fmb – Fumbles – number of times the defensive player (in this case) fumbled the ball

- FR – Fumbles Recovered – number of recoveries of fumbles by either team

- Yds – Yards gained on recovered fumbles

- TD – Touchdowns as a result of a returned fumble recovery

Tackles:

- SK – Sacks – number of times the defending player tackled the quarterback for a loss when the quarterback was attempting to pass the ball

- Comb – Combination of solo tackles (no help) and assisted tackles (multiple defenders involved) (Solo + Ast)

- Solo – number of solo tackles – tackled opponent on own

- Ast – number of assisted tackles – tackled opponent as part of a group of defenders

- TFL – tackles for loss – number of tackles that took place behind the line of scrimmage

- QBHits – number of hits on the quarterback – includes sacks and hits to a QB that did not result in a sack (i.e. as the ball was being thrown)

- Sfty – Safety – number of times the defender tackled a player that resulted in a safety (offensive player was tackled in own end zone)

Context:

Interceptions are mostly the domain of defensive backs (cornerbacks and safeties), but linebackers intercept passes and even a few defensive linemen get in on the action through tipped passes or when they drop back in coverage. Interceptions can certainly denote superior defensive ability, as interceptions are difficult to obtain and can be a game-changer. It is important to note, however, that the best defensive backs may have fewer opportunities to intercept passes as they have fewer passes thrown in their direction. Their ability and reputation often lead to offensive coordinators and quarterbacks choosing to throw fewer passes their way, so interception leaders might mistakenly be thought of as the best pass defenders, which is not true in all cases.

Passes defended is a statistic that merits more discussion. A pass defended occurs when the defensive player deflects or blocks the football in some way which results in the pass not being caught by the receiver. Alternatively, another way to earn a pass defended is to tackle the offensive receiver at the same time the ball arrives, preventing a reception. This stat adds more depth to defender stats by allowing for something other than an interception to be credited to a defensive back. However, good coverage that does not result in a deflection or simultaneous tackle as the ball arrives could still be a very good defensive play, but is not captured in this number.

Fumble statistics are relatively straightforward. Forced fumbles are a major victory for a defender and the defense in general. Being able to strip the ball out of the arms of an offensive player or hit the player with such force that the ball is jarred loose is a big play in the football game and defensive coaches often focus on improving this skill for their defensive players. Fumble recoveries are also recorded and in many cases are a skill. It might appear that a defender was lucky that a ball was fumbled near his position on the field, but being aware and ready to converge on a loose ball is a skill in and of itself, so while there might be some luck involved, there is often considerable skill and grit in earning this statistic.

Sacks are a celebrated statistic for defensive players. Sacks can have a major impact on a game as it forces teams to punt (when preventing a first down), puts teams in poor position to earn a first down (when it occurs on earlier downs), can force offensive teams to settle for a field goal instead of a touchdown, and can take teams out of field goal range and force a punt rather than points. Individual speed and strength contribute to sacks, but defensive scheme and the presence of other strong pass rushers on the defensive roster also are important factors in determining this statistic.

Tackles are a welcome addition to defensive statistics as it counts the number of times a player either made a tackle on their own (solo) or with other defenders (Ast). In general, this is a good statistic for defensive players, although there are exceptions, such as defensive backs who rack up a high number of tackles could be due to poor performance in defending passes, resulting in them needing to tackle the receiver they were attempting to stop from catching the pass.

Tackles for loss (TFL) and quarterback hits (QBHits) are also valuable statistics for defenders as tackling players for a loss makes earning a first down on that series for the offense even more difficult. Also, hitting the quarterback, even when not resulting in a sack, can have a cumulative effect to deteriorate quarterback play throughout the course of the game and is valuable in and of itself. Safeties, although rare, can change the nature of a game. A safety results in two points for the team and the other team must now punt the ball, resulting in the team earning the safety to gain points and get the ball. This statistic rewards the player who led to the end result of a safety on a play.

Waterfall Chart

For this section, we'll introduce a new chart called a waterfall chart. A waterfall chart is useful to show increases or decreases over time or a summation to a whole of some particular metric. For our defensive stats, let's first get the basic statistics from *Pro Football Reference* for defensive players from:

https://www.pro-football-reference.com/years/2019/defense.htm (due to restrictions, the file exported to Excel will only include the top 500 defensive players). This is fine for our sample, but if you want the full sample, you can obtain it by downloading as a CSV file and then loading into Excel. In some versions of Excel, this may be your only option to download this data.

We will construct a waterfall chart for solo tackles, by player, for one team. After you have the data set in Excel, we will sort by team. To do this:

1) *Highlight Row 2*

2) Data – Filter Button

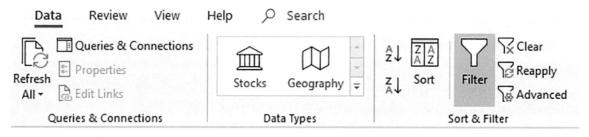

3) *Click the drop down in C2 – uncheck select all – scroll down and check SFO for San Francisco's Defense*

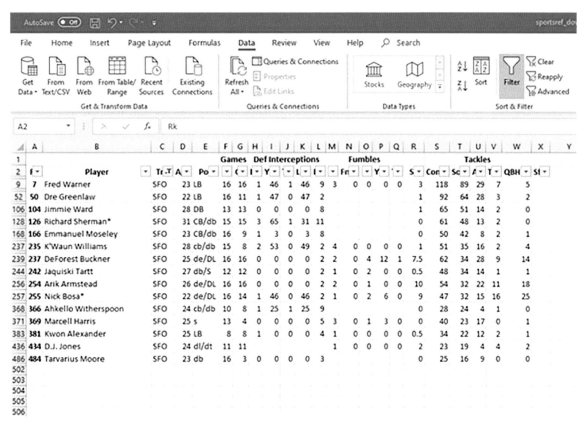

		Games		Def	Interceptions						Fumbles							Tackles				
#	Player	Tr	A	Po	(G)	I	Y	I	L	I	Fn	I	Y	I	S	Con	Sc	A	T	QBH	Sf
7	Fred Warner	SFO	23	LB	16	16	1	46	1	46	9	3	0	0	0	0	3	118	89	29	7	5
50	Dre Greenlaw	SFO	22	LB	16	11	1	47	0	47	2					1	92	64	28	3	2
104	Jimmie Ward	SFO	28	DB	13	13	0	0	0	0	8					1	65	51	14	2	0
126	Richard Sherman*	SFO	31	CB/db	15	15	3	65	1	31	11					0	61	48	13	2	0
166	Emmanuel Moseley	SFO	23	CB/db	16	9	1	3	0	3	8					0	50	42	8	2	1
235	K'Waun Williams	SFO	28	cb/db	15	8	2	53	0	49	2	4	0	0	0	0	1	51	35	16	2	4
237	DeForest Buckner	SFO	25	de/DL	16	16	0	0	0	0	2	2	0	4	12	1	7.5	62	34	28	9	14
242	Jaquiski Tartt	SFO	27	db/S	12	12	0	0	0	0	2	1	0	2	0	0	0.5	48	34	14	1	1
254	Arik Armstead	SFO	26	de/DL	16	16	0	0	0	0	2	2	0	1	0	0	10	54	32	22	11	18
255	Nick Bosa*	SFO	22	de/DL	16	14	1	46	0	46	2	1	0	2	6	0	9	47	32	15	16	25
366	Ahkello Witherspoon	SFO	24	cb/db	10	8	1	25	1	25	9						0	28	24	4	1	0
369	Marcell Harris	SFO	25	s	13	4	0	0	0	0	5	3	0	1	3	0	0	40	23	17	0	1
381	Kwon Alexander	SFO	25	LB	8	8	1	0	0	0	4	1	0	0	0	0	0.5	34	22	12	2	1
434	D.J. Jones	SFO	24	dl/dt	11	11					1		0	0	0	0	2	23	19	4	4	2
484	Tarvarius Moore	SFO	23	db	16	3	0	0	0	0	3						0	25	16	9	0	0

4) *Highlight the data in column T* (include the header)

5) Insert – Charts – Waterfall, Funnel, … Charts – Waterfall (first option)

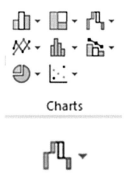

Charts

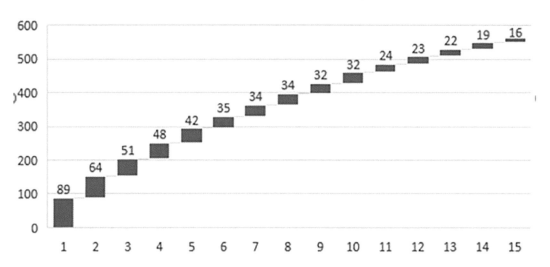

6) Add player names to horizontal axis – Design – Select Data – Horizontal (Category Axis Labels) – Edit – *Highlight names in column B* (do not include header)

7) Remove legend – Add Chart Element – Legend – None

8) Label Axes – Add Chart Element – Axis Titles (do one at a time to add both) – label

9) *Add Title*

10) Change color to gold – click on chart – ***paintbrush***, scroll down to gold/yellow

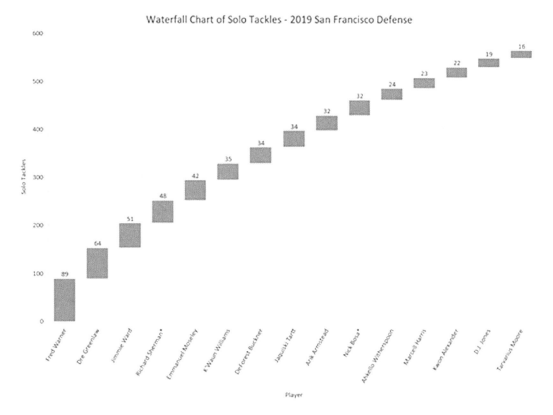

The waterfall chart shows the progression from most to fewest solo tackles for defensive players on the 49ers. It sums across the defenders and you can see the total rise with each subsequent bar. At the end of the horizontal axis, you arrive at the total number of solo tackles in this sample for the 49ers (read off of the vertical axis). Along the way, you see the players with the highest solo tackles (Warner and Greenlaw) and get a feel for the distribution as the number of solo tackles falls as our eyes move left-to-right.

Audible: Fred Warner's Season – Game-by-Game

Let's take a closer look at top tackler Fred Warner's season using his gamelog. His gamelog is available at: https://www.pro-football-reference.com/players/W/WarnFr00/gamelog/2019/. Remove the summary line at the end and we'll use each game of the regular season to map out how many solo and tackles and assists he had each week throughout the season. To do with we'll use a combination graph of columns and line.

To begin a Combination Chart:

1) *Highlight N2:O18*

2) Insert – Charts – Insert Combo Chart

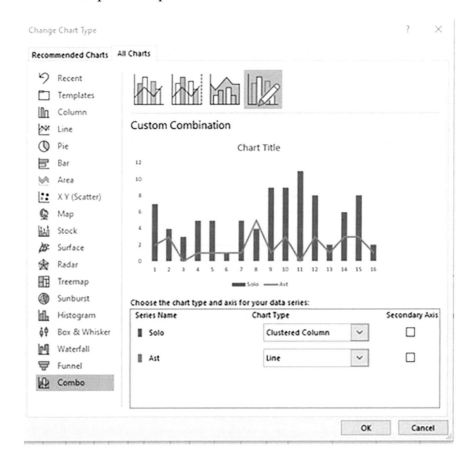

3) We'll use the default, but if go to Type – Change Chart Type you will see different drop-down options for each series

4) Let's change the horizontal axis to by Opponent: Select Data – Horizontal (Category) Axis Labels – Edit – *Highlight H3:H18*

5) Add Chart Element – Axis Title – Primary Vertical – Add Title

6) Add Title

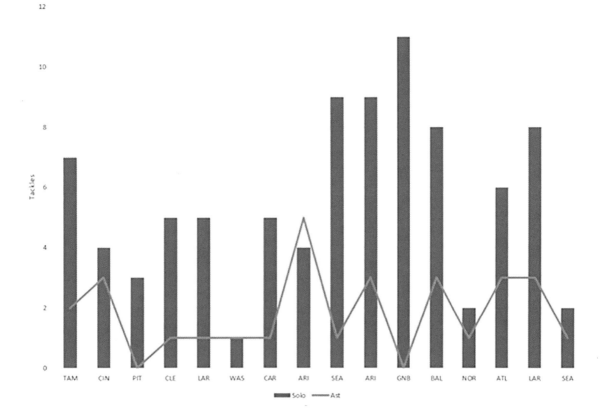

Fred Warner - San Francisco - Solo Tackles and Assists - 2019 Season

The combo chart allows the viewer to see the number of solo tackles and assists, per week, over the course of the 2019 season for Warner. You immediately notice he only had one game where his assists exceeded his solo tackles (vs. Arizona the first time), the week where he had double-digit solo tackles (vs. Green Bay) and other high points of 8+ solo tackles (Seattle, Arizona, Baltimore, LA Rams). He had a particularly successful season on a team that won the NFC championship. Comparing his season to others on the San

Francisco roster or to players on your favorite team is a straightforward exercise following similar steps to those listed above.

Moving Forward: Suggested Story Telling with Data to Pursue:

1) Players on which teams created the most turnovers (interceptions and fumbles) on defense?

2) How closely related are Sacks and QB hits? Which players had many QB hits, but not many sacks?

3) Choose your favorite defensive player and map out his season game-by-game highlighting his best statistics.

CHAPTER 12

ADVANCED DEFENSE

The advanced defensive statistics add even more detail to defensive player performance. The sections of the advanced data on *Pro Football Reference* begin with basic player info (name, team, age, position, games, games started) and then are broken into Pass Coverage, Pass Rush, and Tackles groups. The relevant stats in each category are described below:

Pass Coverage

- Int – Interceptions (same as in basic defense)

- Tgt – Targets – number of times the offensive receiver who the defender was covering had the ball thrown in his direction by the quarterback

- Cmp – completions when targeted – conditional on being targeted, how many receptions were made by the offensive player in this situation

- Cmp% - Completions when targeted (Cmp) divided by Targets (Tgt)

- Yds – Yards allowed on completions (when targeted)

- Yds/Cmp – Yards allowed per completion

- Yds/Tgt – Yards allowed per target

- TD – Touchdowns allowed when targeted

- Rat – QB rating on plays where defender was targeted

- DADOT – Average depth of target when targeted as a defender (how far beyond the line of scrimmage was the intended pass when targeted)

- Air – sum of air yards on completions when targeted

- YAC – Yards after catch for the receiver when the defender was targeted

Pass Rush

- Bltz – number of times the defensive player blitzed on the season

- Hrry – number of quarterback hurries by the defender – QB threw before intended or was rushed out of the pocket

- QBKD – Quarterback knockdowns – number of times the defender caused the QB to hit the ground on a hit during/after a throw

- SK – Sacks (same as in basic defensive stats)

- Prss – QB pressures – sum of hurries, knockdowns, and sacks by the defensive player

Tackles

- Comb – Combination of solo and assisted tackles (same as basic defensive stats)

- MTkl – Missed tackles – number of times a defender should have made a tackle, but was unsuccessful

- MTkl% - Missed tackle percentage – missed tackles divided by the sum of missed and combined tackles (sum of solo and assisted tackles)

Context:

The advanced statistics for pass coverage expand the information to include targets. Targets (Tgt) are when the defender was covering the intended receiver of a pass. We would expect great coverage players to have fewer targets, as passing plays would be designed to go away from these defenders. Defensive backs playing opposite an elite defender often receive more targets due to the game planning noted above. Once targets are established, statistics are computed for completions and completion percentage when targeted. This puts the number of receiver receptions in proper context for a defending player as it notes/calculates these receptions in terms of how many passes were thrown to the receiver he was covering. Along similar lines, yardage on these plays and computed averages (per completion and per target) again put context on the defensive ability of the players defending passes.

Adding QB Rating on targeted plays is also a useful figure for a quick comparison of defenders as this rating considers not only the averages (per completion or target) but events such as touchdowns and interceptions. DADOT is a difficult anagram to decipher, but it refers to the average depth of the target when targeted as a defender. In other words, how far down the field (beyond the line of scrimmage) is the defender being targeted? The further downfield the target, the more the defending player is relying upon pressure to disrupt the throw. Being unsuccessful at defending short targets could be due to lack of physicality or first step in defending quick throws such as slants by wide receivers or tight ends or getting into coverage for backs coming out of the backfield.

The type of coverage system typically employed by the defense (or more likely what type of defense was being played on that particular play) will influence these numbers. For instance, man coverage (one-on-one) with or without safety support or a zone defense elicits different responsibilities for a defending player. The outcome of a play could be influenced by multiple receivers in a particular zone or "pick" plays (when not flagged) to create space for a receiver. Air sums the yardage that the pass attempts were made in a defender's direction, while yards after catch (YAC) gives some insight into tackling ability or position on the field when the ball was caught (if the receiver intends to catch the pass and go out of bounds to stop the clock, then YAC was not the goal of the play design).

The Pass Rush category of advanced statistics on *Pro Football Reference* gives details on the number of times a player blitzed, the number of hurries of the quarterback he had, the number of times he knocked the quarterback down, and his number of sacks. Pressures combines hurries, knockdowns, and sacks. Defensive linemen, unless they sometimes play linebacker, will not be credited with blitzes as they nearly always rush on passing plays (in zone blitz schemes they may drop into coverage as other defenders' blitz). Linebackers and defensive backs, on the other hand, will only get pressure on the quarterback when they do blitz. Therefore, taking ratios of these variables are not helpful for linemen, but could be insightful for other defensive positions.

The last couple of columns under tackles adds missed tackles (MTkl) and missed tackle percentage (MTkl%) to tackling statistics. Combining tackles with missed tackles gives an overall feel for how often that player was involved in a play. While missed tackles are always bad, by definition, some will occur due to great moves by offensive players. While missed tackle percentage on its own is a great statistic, considering the sum of both Comb and MTkl may also give some helpful information (i.e. young players that are in position to make tackles show the athletic ability to get to the ball carrier and, perhaps, with practice of better tackling skills/strategy, could turn into an even better defensive player).

Combination Chart

For the advanced defensive statistics, let's do an example with defenders covering the pass. We'll first download the data into Excel from *Pro Football Reference* at https://www.pro-football-reference.com/years/2019/defense_advanced.htm. We'll work on a combo chart for the defenders that were targeted the most during the 2019 season. To get a workable subset of this data, we'll first sort. Highlight row 2 (where there are the header names) and go to Data – Filter. This will allow the data to be filtered by any of these columns, using the headers. We'll use Targets (Tgt), so we'll sort by row I, from largest to smallest. We'll take the top 20 and will look at completion percentage (Cmp%) when they were targeted and passer rating (Rat) when they were targeted. To do this:

1) *Highlight K2:K22* and then *CNTL-Highlight P2:P22*

2) Insert – Charts – Insert Combo Chart

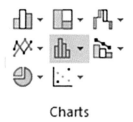

Charts

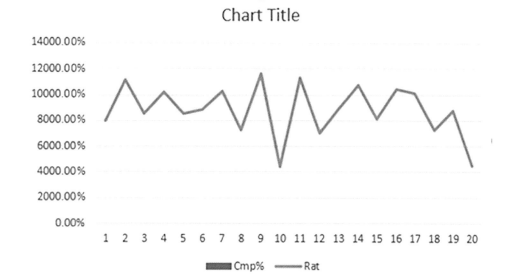

Immediately we notice this does not look correct. We only see the orange line (Rat), but not the blue line (Cmp%). In addition, the vertical axis looks very strange in terms of the numbers presented. Given that these two figures are on such a different scale (one in percentages and the other not), the default combo chart does not work. This can be easily rectified, however, by using a secondary axis. To do this, continue to follow these steps:

3) Click on Chart – Chart Tools – Design - on Ribbon go to Change Chart Type – new window appears

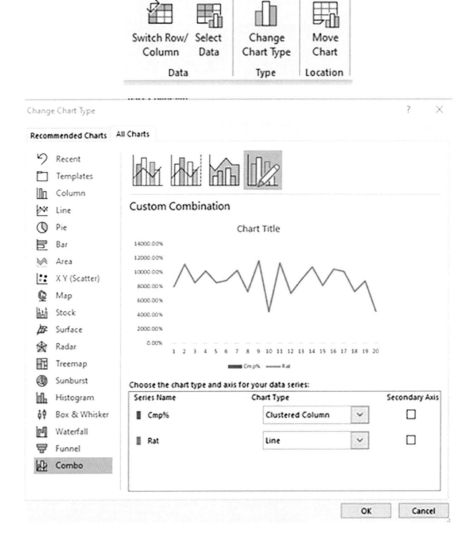

4) For Rat (Rating) – check the box for secondary axis – click ok – new chart appears

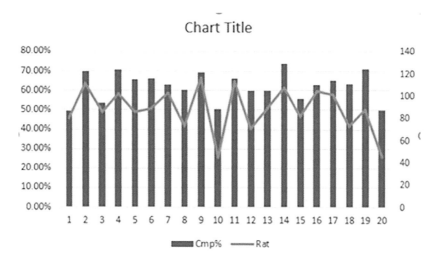

There is now a secondary axis (right-hand side) that shows the scale for Rating, while the scale for Completion Percentage is shown on the left-hand side vertical axis

5) Change Horizontal Axis to player names (Select Data – Horizontal (Category) Axis Labels) – Edit – *Highlight B3:B22*)

6) *Change Axis Titles and Add Chart Title*

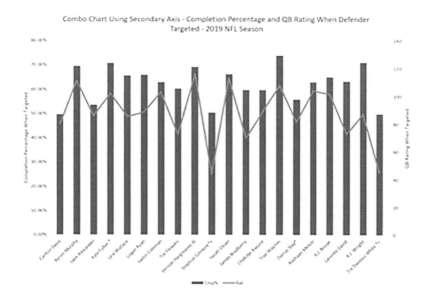

The combo chart using a secondary axis allows us to compare these defenders across two statistics which are measured differently. What insights can we gain by examining this chart of the most-targeted defensive players in the passing game? First, we see the general success of preventing completions for Carlton Davis, Stephon Gilmore, and Tre'Davious White. Furthermore, we see how great Gilmore and White were (even compared to Davis) in terms of preventing opposing QB success in terms of generating low QB Ratings when targeted. Other players were not as successful in 2019, including instances with relatively high completion percentages against and high QB ratings when targeted such as Byron Murphy, Vernon Hargreaves III, Isiah Oliver, and Trae Waynes. KJ Wright is an interesting case as he allowed over 70% completion percentage when targeted but kept QB Rating below 90 despite the receivers catching the ball in front of him.

Let's further the story by comparing KJ Wright to Vernon Hargreaves III. With each allowing around 70% completion percentage, it would seem to be a somewhat fair comparison, but is it really? First, KJ Wright is a linebacker, while Vernon Hargreaves III is a corner back. Therefore, they are likely facing different types of receivers (running backs and tight ends vs. wide receivers) with different abilities and different targeted lengths by quarterbacks (shorter routes vs. longer routes). To explore further, let's continue to use the advanced defensive statistics from Pro Football Reference and isolate these two players and then compare some stats that we did not observe in the previous chart.

1) Using the downloaded Advanced Defensive Statistics – *highlight row 2*

2) Data – Filter (to create filters for each column below row 2)

3) Click on the down arrow in column B (Player) – uncheck Select All – find our two players (KJ Wright and Vernon Hargreaves III and check each box) – now our data set is confined to two players

4) *Highlight header and data in column M* (header and 2 observations) – *CTRL-copy each of the following: columns N, O, and Q* (header and 2 observations each)

5) Insert – Charts – 2D Column

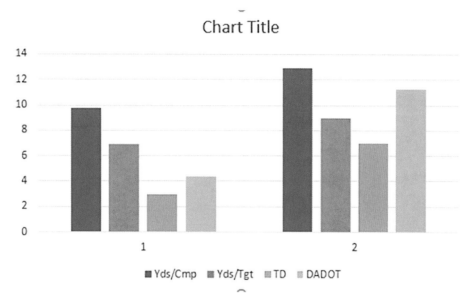

This is not really what we want, so we need to make some adjustments.

6) In Chart Tools – Design – on ribbon go to Data – Select Data – Switch Row/Column

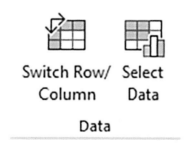

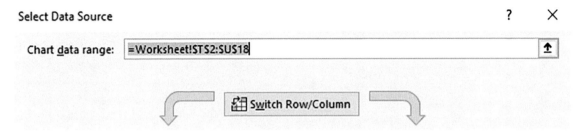

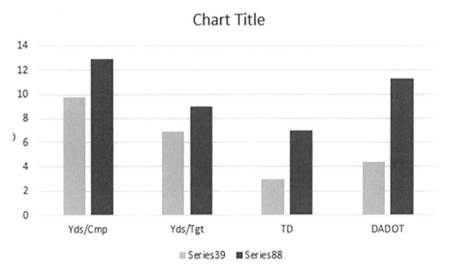

7) Data – Select Data – Legend Entries (Series)

    a) highlight Series 39 – Edit – *Highlight K.J. Wright in column B*

    b) highlight Series 88 – Edit – *Highlight Vernon Hargreaves III in column B*

8) 8) *Add descriptive title to chart*

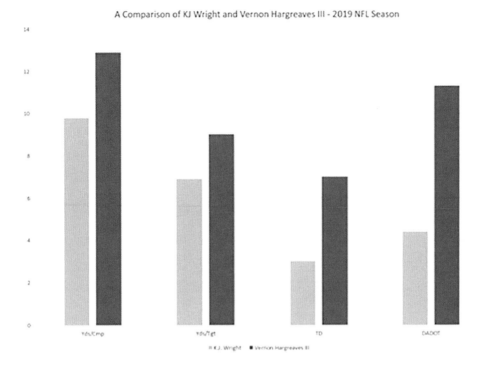

A Comparison of KJ Wright and Vernon Hargreaves III - 2019 NFL Season

We can see from the chart that the totals on Hargreaves III are greater than for Wright across all four statistics, in many cases by a considerable margin. Hargreaves allowed a higher Yards per Completion and Yards per Attempt than Wright and more than double the touchdowns (7 vs. 3). The far-right component of the graph, however, illustrates the great difference between where the two players were targeted (DADOT). Passes thrown in Hargreaves direction were thrown over twice as far down the field as passes thrown to receivers when Wright was in coverage. This helps to explain the difference in Yards per Completion and Yards per Target. We can still conclude that Wright did a good job in preventing TDs and keeping the Yards per Completion relatively low, resulting in a lower figure for QB Rating when passes were thrown in his direction, but the way in which he was targeted was quite different from the manner in which Hargreaves was thrown against. You can find other comparisons by comparing each of these players to others who played the same position and were targeted similarly. Use the filters in Excel to identify these players and see what charts you can use to illustrate the differences in players you identify.

Moving Forward: Suggested Story Telling with Data to Pursue:

1) Compare any two defensive players in terms of their pass rushing ability (similar to what was done above with pass coverage).

2) What players had the most missed tackles (or highest percentage of missed tackles)? Did these players make up for this deficiency by being good pass rushers?

3) Choose one of the top defensive backs and look at their game-by-game results. What happened to their targets as the season went on? How did the next team on the schedule respond (in terms of throwing passes in their direction) after a particularly great or sub-par game?

CHAPTER 13

ADDITIONAL FOOTBALL ANALYTICS RESOURCES

Although this book has focused on *Pro Football Reference* for data to start the process of creating charts and analyzing football statistics, there are many other terrific resources for you to read and use. Before moving to them, however, there are still a number of areas on *Pro Football Reference* that we did not have time to cover in the book. You can use the same sort of analysis and charts that we have been doing to look even deeper into the numbers in these sections.

Some sections of the *Pro Football Reference* website that we did not have time to cover includes player data on scrimmage stats, kick and punt returns, and scoring. These are available under the 2019 season player stats and are listed in the standard section. Advanced stats, available in the same place, include team advanced stats, which looks at the advanced stats aggregated by team.

If you enjoy fantasy football, a game where you draft a lineup of players and compete against others on a weekly basis, *Pro Football Reference* also has fantasy statistics for your examination. Following this link: https://www.pro-football-reference.com/years/2019/fantasy.htm gives you a breakdown of individual player statistics and fantasy scoring in four categories which relate to standard fantasy scoring, point-per-reception leagues, and the two main daily fantasy gaming websites (DraftKings and FanDuel). Also available in the general fantasy section are links to Red Zone performance for passing, rushing, and receiving. The Red Zone is the area on the field inside the opponent's 20-yard line. The ability to score touchdowns in the red zone is often the difference between winning and losing games. The statistics available on *Pro Football Reference* provide insights into how players at key fantasy positions did in this area of the field for the 2019 season. Beyond these statistics, *Pro Football Reference* has many other resources including historical results by year, leader boards, All-Pro teams, the draft, etc. I encourage you to open a page that interests you, download the data, and see what you can learn by generating charts on your own.

Beyond *Pro Football Reference*, there are many other football websites for you to explore. Some of my favorites are NFL.com, Pro Football Focus, Warren Sharp's Football Preview, and Football Outsiders. An overview of these sites is given below.

NFL.com

NFL.com is the official website of the National Football League. While it has a plethora of features, it also offers detailed statistics on the players and teams. The direct link to the statistics page is: https://www.nfl.com/stats/player-stats/. The website offers a variety of performance statistics at the individual and team level. Although not as deep as the data we see on *Pro Football Reference*, it does offer some statistics that are not seen on the other sites. A major move forward for football analytics is the availability of Next Gen Stats, which you can link to through the page above or directly at: https://nextgenstats.nfl.com/stats/top-plays/fastest-ball-carriers. Here you see a variety of valuable and informative statistics for Top Plays, Passing, Rushing, and Receiving. Like the *Pro Football Reference* site, NFL.com has many years of data to explore.

Pro Football Focus

Pro Football Focus is an elite football analytics site which can be accessed at: https://www.pff.com/. Although much of the site is for subscribers, after seeing what they have available, you may be interested in unlocking its content. This site goes deep in terms of player analysis and has tons of data you cannot find anywhere else. Their tracking of games and being able to create stats in all game situations is a testament to their dedication to the sport. They work with all 32 NFL teams and many college football programs as well.

Sharp Football Analysis

One of the pure treasures of summer in recent years is the football annual published by Warren Sharp. His website is www.sharpfootballanalysis.com and his book is available in PDF form directly on the site (the traditional book is also available there and through outlets such as Amazon). His colorful book goes in-depth on each team, giving an overall breakdown of the past season's performance in addition to a preview of the upcoming season. He has valuable data on team spending by position, game-to-game metrics from each week of the season, statistics on rest and health, play tendencies, snap rates, directional running and passing statistics, success by personnel groupings, and a whole lot more. It is a tremendously valuable resource both looking back on last season and looking forward to the next one. Reading the book and comparing teams will give you a greater knowledge of the game and is certain to generate creative thoughts for you to pursue in terms of creating charts and analysis on your own.

Football Outsiders

Another terrific annual that comes out every summer is the Football Outsiders Almanac. It's accompanying website, www.footballoutsiders.com, provides a seemingly endless supply of insights and statistics for you to peruse and use. Their book has a profile of every player, arranged by position, in addition to team sections giving an overview of the organization including a review of last season and a preview of the upcoming one.

Their statistics, directly available on their site and featured in their annual, includes DVOA and DYAR which puts each play into context related to situation and opposing defense. They use these stats, and many others, to provide analysis and insights both in their book (coming in at nearly 500 pages a year) and their website. The book and website will further provide you with knowledge of both the game of football and the use of statistics.

POST-GAME

Thank you very much for the purchase of this book. I hope it leads to a lifelong love and use of statistics, excel skills, visualizations, analytics, and insights into football.

We are interested in your next steps. Please send us your visualizations (use a screenshot if possible) and we will try to post them on our website at www.seesports.net. We would love to show your work off to the world. Please send us an email with your charts/visualizations to info@seesports.net. Be sure to include your first name, last initial, city and state, and a note saying it would be fine to post your chart on our website.

See the First Steps: Football Analytics is also available as a video book. Please go to www.SeeSports.net for additional information. SEE Sports is looking forward to publishing additional analytics books, as well as conducting summer camps for teens and workshops for adults. Please visit www.SeeSports.net to look for updates and sign up for the newsletter and blogs. You can also email at info@seesports.net to contact us. We look forward to hearing from you. Have fun and enjoy football!

Made in the USA
Middletown, DE
13 August 2021